D1234269

Economical &
Nutritional Diets
Using Scarce Resources

. . . .

MSU International Business
& Economic Studies

Economical &
Nutritional Diets
Using Scarce Resources

. . . .
. . . .

JOSÉ DAVID LANGIER

Senior Economist
Department of Economic Affairs
Pan American Union, Washington, D.C.

. . . .

Institute for International Business
        & Economic Development Studies
Division of Research
Graduate School of Business Administration
Michigan State University

to my parents

v

: : : : : : : :**CONTENTS** :

LIST OF FIGURES

LIST OF TABLES

. . . .

PREFACE

. . . .

This book tries to integrate problems in the areas of nutrition, economics, and programming. The nutritionist will be especially interested in Chapter 1, the first section of Chapter 2, Chapter 4, and 5. The economist will find Chapters 1, 2, 3, and 5 of particular interest. The student of programming methods will want to read the last section of Chapter 2 and Chapter 4.

The book is based on my Ph.D. thesis presented to the Department of Economics, Michigan State University. The thesis, and in consequence the book, was made possible by a fellowship from the Economic and Agricultural Development Institute, a predecessor of the Institute for International Business and Economic Development Studies, Graduate School of Business Administration, Michigan State University. I express my gratitude to this institute for its financial support. Most of all, I express my gratitude to Prof. Victor E. Smith for his truly patient help.

While I assume full responsibility for any mistakes, I would also like to thank the Division of Research, Graduate School of Business Administration, Michigan State University, for their editing and production assistance. Finally, I am grateful to Marta Elliott for her help.

xiii

ACKNOWLEDGMENTS

Appreciation is hereby expressed to the Division of Research, Graduate School of Business Administration, Michigan State University, for permission to quote extensively from:

Smith, Victor E. *Electronic Computation of Human Diets*. East Lansing: Bureau of Business and Economic Research, Graduate School of Business Administration, Michigan State University, 1964.

and to the University of Chicago Press for permission to quote extensively from:

Lancaster, K. J. "A New Approach to Consumer Theory." *Journal of Political Economy* 74 (April 1966): 132-57.

1

PROBLEM

and background

. . . .

MANY LOW-INCOME FAMILIES AND INHABITANTS OF UNDERDEVELOPED regions do not achieve one or more of the allowances of essential nutrients recommended by nutritionists. Aside from its humanistic considerations, malnutrition may cause disease, temporary or permanent damage to an individual's physical or mental health, even brain damage. Hence, the work capacity of the undernourished man is smaller than that of a healthy one. A vicious circle of poverty-malnutrition-poverty can be formed: because of their poverty, the people are undernourished; malnutrition reduces their productivity; low productivity keeps them poor; etc. Elimination of existing malnutrition is one way of breaking this vicious circle.

The governments of countries in which malnutrition exists are trying to improve the nutritional status of their populations by increasing the supplies of existing foods, by introducing new foods into the existing food consumption pattern, and by changing food habits. Because the resources of both families and countries are scarce, there is a need to be economical. Therefore, a big problem is deciding among the different alternatives — which food production and consumption to increase, which new foods to introduce.

Nutritionists, geographers, and economists have developed measures for evaluating the nutritional contributions of foods which fall into three basic methodological categories. The first, or conventional, method considers only one nutrient and finds the most economical food that will provide that nutrient. The second method considers all the essential nutrients that a food will supply, but regards all nutrients as equally important. The third method considers nutrients as being of different importance but assigns weights arbitrarily. New methods for measuring the nutritional contribution of foods are needed which take all the essential nutrients into account, weight nutrients according to their relevance in particular situations, and can be applied to find economical foods where malnutrition exists.

There is a mathematical method that gives economical solutions for improving diets, without using a measure of the nutritional contribution of food. The diet obtained by employing this mathematical method (linear programming) eliminates the nutritional deficiencies at minimum cost. Perhaps because it requires mathematics, nutritionists have not yet made much use of this method.

MEASUREMENTS BY NUTRITIONISTS

Nutritionists have used different methods in deriving inexpensive diets for low-income families. The conventional method of finding the nutrient-per-dollar ratio is most clearly presented by Tremolières, Serville, and Jacquot.[1] They group foods into three categories: those foods rich in animal protein, in calories, and in vitamin C. To obtain the amount of nutrient-per-dollar of a food, they first find the amount of the edible portion in the food sold at the retail level, then get the amount of the nutrient furnished in the edible portion, and finally divide this quantity by the retail price of the food.

If E_j is the proportion of food j as sold at the retail level that is edible, N_{ij} is the amount of nutrient i obtained from 1 kilogram of the edible portion of food j and p_j is the price of 1 kilogram of food j at the retail level, then:

$$T_{ij} = \frac{E_j N_{ij}}{p_j}$$

where T_{ij} = quantity of nutrient i consumed per dollar if food j is purchased

           $i = 1, \ldots, m$

           $j = 1, \ldots, q.$

. . . .

1. J. Tremolières, Y. Serville, and R. Jacquot, *La Pratique de l'Aliméntation*, Vol. 3, Chap. 3.

The food with the largest T_{ij} is the most economical source of nutrient i.

Wilson, Fisher, and Fuqua[2] compare the percentage of a single nutrient which a given group of foods provides in the diet with the percentage of the total cost of the diet which this group of foods represents. Again, the group of foods with the largest ratio is the most economical one providing that nutrient in the diet. They use this measure of efficiency for each of the several nutrients that a group of foods supplies. Wilson, Fisher, and Fuqua's measure can also be applied to a single food instead of a group of foods, indicating the cheapest source of a given nutrient in the diet.

If the problem is to improve nutritionally deficient diets and to save resources for uses other than food, then Tremolières, Serville, and Jacquot's method is appropriate only when malnutrition involves just one nutrient. Wilson, Fisher, and Fuqua's method is a variant of the conventional method which gives a nutrient-per-dollar ratio, but has the disadvantage of only being applicable to foods in the actual diet.[3] When there is more than one nutritional deficiency, both methods are inappropriate because the nutritional contribution of a food includes *all* the essential nutrients that a food furnishes. To be sure, Tremolières, Serville, and Jacquot know that a food provides more than one essential nutrient when consumed, but their method considers only one nutrient as the nutritional contribution of a food. In each case, of course, they attempt to consider that nutrient for which the food is most important.

Terroine[4] takes into account the fact that a food supplies more than one nutrient by placing the foods in tabular form, in which the rows are the different foods and the columns are the essential nutrients. In the intersection of a row with a column he writes in the T_{ij}'s of Tremolières, Serville, and Jacquot's method (the i represents the nutrient, or column, and the j represents the food, or row). Then he classifies the food according to the number of times that the food

. . . .

2. E. D. Wilson, K. H. Fisher, and M. E. Fuqua, *Principles of Nutrition,* Chap. 18.

3. Victor E. Smith, *Electronic Computation of Human Diets,* pp. 61-7, presents a more elaborate criticism of methods such as that of Wilson, Fisher, and Fuqua.

4. E. F. Terroine, "Valeur Aliméntaire et Coût des Denrées," *Annales de la Nutrition et de l'Aliméntation* 16 (1962): 91-172.

appears as the most or second most economical food furnishing a single nutrient. He ranks the food with the largest number of such appearances in first place, the food with the second largest number in second, and so on.

Because Terroine considers only the nutrients that are the most or the second most economically provided by the food, he still eliminates other nutritional contributions of a food that may be relevant to improving nutritional status. To show how Terroine's method distorts the choice of a food to ameliorate the nutritional status of a family, consider a family with three nutritional deficiencies that wants to spend $1 for improving its nutritional intake. Suppose there are two foods, X and Y, such that X is the cheapest source of two deficient nutrients and furnishes only those two nutrients, while Y is the third most economical source of the three deficient nutrients and only provides these three nutrients. Either $.99 expended on X or $1 expended on Y will supply the family with a nutritional intake equal to the recommended allowances of the two nutrients that X furnishes. However, $1 expended on Y will provide a larger amount of the third deficient nutrient that could be provided by the expenditure of the $.01 left from the expenditure on X, on Z the cheapest source of this nutrient. Using Terroine's method, Y will not be considered, although it improves the nutritional status of the family to a larger degree than the combination of X and Z described above.

A forgotten pioneer work by Sherman and Gillet[5] developed a measure of the "composite value" of the nutrient content of a food. They divided the amounts of the nutrients furnished in the edible portion of 1 pound of a food by the respective recommended allowances, weighted these ratios by two different sets of weights, and then added them to get the "composite value" for the food. They considered calories, protein, calcium, phosphorus, and iron, as these were the only nutrients for which nutritionists recommended allowances at the time of their study. The two sets of weights suggested were: a) 60, 10, 10, 10, and 10; and b) 40, 15, 15, 15, and 15 for each of the above nutrients, respectively. These weights were arbitrary, but took into account the fact that calories were often deficient in the diets of poor American families.

. . . .

5. H. C. Sherman and L. R. Gillet, *The Adequacy and Economy of Some City Dietaries*, p. 20. I thank Dr. C. Florencio, Department of Foods and Nutrition, Michigan State University, for bringing this work to my attention.

This calculation showed remarkable sophistication for the time. However, when malnutrition exists, using these weights to evaluate the nutritional contribution of food may distort the choice of the most economical food because the weights are not adequate measures of the sizes of the deficiencies. The measurement may also distort the choice of the most economical food because it includes non-deficient nutrients in the nutritional contribution of food.

In 1965, Davis[6] proposed a measure of the multiple contribution of food, using the following method. He took the amount of a nutrient in the edible portion of a food as purchased and divided it by the recommended allowance of this nutrient. He added these ratios for the vitamins and minerals (vitamins A, D, C, thiamin, riboflavin, niacin, calcium, and iron) and divided their sum by eight, the number of vitamins and minerals considered. Then he summed this average value with the similar relatives for calories and protein and divided it by three. Finally, he divided this last average by the price of 100 grams of the food as purchased, obtaining an "overall economic-nutritional index."

In 1966, Armstrong[7] calculated "overall economic-nutritional indices" for Canada using Canadian prices and seven instead of eight vitamins and minerals (he did not consider vitamin D in his study). If N_{cj} is the amount of calories in the edible portion of 100 grams of food j as purchased, N_{pj} is the amount of protein in the edible portion of 100 grams of food j as purchased, N_{ij} is the amount of vitamin or mineral i in the edible portion of 100 grams of food j as purchased, R_c, R_p, and R_i are the recommended allowances of calories, protein, and vitamin or mineral i, and p_j is the price of 100 grams of food j as purchased, then:

$$D_j = \frac{\dfrac{\dfrac{N_{cj}}{R_c} + \dfrac{N_{pj}}{R_p} + \dfrac{1}{m+v} \sum\limits_{i=1}^{m+v} \dfrac{N_{ij}}{R_i}}{3}}{p_j}$$

· · · · · · · ·

6. J. G. Davis, "The Nutritional Index and Economic Nutritional Index of Foods," *Dairy Industries* 30 (1965): 193-97.

7. J. G. Armstrong, "An Economic-Nutritional Index of Foods," *Canadian Nutrition Notes* 22 (1966): 25-39.

where $D_j =$ "overall economic-nutritional index" of food j as pur-
        chased using Davis' method

$j = 1, \ldots, q$
$m =$ number of minerals in the study
$v =$ number of vitamins in the study.

The food with the largest D_j has the largest nutritional contribution per dollar, by Davis' method.

To sum the essential nutrients of a food implies giving them weights that represent their nutritional importance. By considering the vitamins and minerals as one nutrient, the "protective" nutrient, Davis and Armstrong give weights to the vitamins and minerals that are different from the ones given to the calories and protein, although the "protective" nutrient as a whole has the same weight. For Davis, 1 percent of the recommended allowance of a vitamin or of a mineral is equivalent to 1/8 percent of the recommended allowance of calories or protein. For Armstrong, 1 percent of the recommended allowance of a vitamin or of a mineral is equivalent to 1/7 percent of the recommended allowance of calories or protein. It seems that the weight (nutritional importance) of vitamins and minerals should not depend upon the number of them in a given study!

When Davis' method is applied to find the food which makes the largest nutritional contribution to improve the nutritional status of families with deficient intake, it considers nutrients whose consumption may have already reached the recommended allowance and, therefore, distorts the choice of the food to consume. Certain nutrient deficiencies may be larger than others, and because of this, they may be more important than others. Davis himself pointed out that "some nutritionists consider that protein is by far the most important aspect because it is in protein that the diets of the poorest nations are the most deficient."[8]

In summary, certain nutritionists' approaches to measuring the nutritional contribution of food fail to consider all the essential nutrients that a food provides. Others that take all the essential nutrients into account do not give them weights relevant to the particular situation.

. . . .

8. Davis, "Nutritional Index," p. 194.

MEASUREMENTS BY GEOGRAPHERS AND ECONOMISTS

During World War I, Cooper and Spillman[9] compared the efficiency of land when used for the production of different foods. First they found the average quantity of a food produced on 1 acre of land, dividing the total production of this food by the total acreage utilized to obtain this output. Then they calculated the amount of this average that is edible, and finally they obtained the amount of calories and protein in the edible portion.

To increase the availability of calories they suggested increasing the output of the food with the largest calories-per-acre ratio. They proposed the same for protein. Because it considers only one nutrient and disregards the other nutritional contributions of the food, the conventional method as applied by Cooper and Spillman is not suitable when there is need to increase the output of more than one nutrient at the same time.

In 1958, Stamp[10] used caloric output as the single indicator of the nutritional contribution of food to measure the efficiency of land used for the production of different foods, reasoning that food output was of such a variety that all the other nutrients would also be provided. This actually avoided the problem of measuring the nutritional contribution of food, because all the other essential nutrients that are furnished by foods were not considered.

An economist named Christensen[11] suggested a method in 1943, 22 years before Davis proposed his method, of measuring the total nutritional value of food that takes all the essential nutrients contained in a food into account. His method divides the amount of a nutrient in a food by the recommended allowance of this nutrient, adds all such relatives for a given food, then divides the sum by the number of all nutrients considered.

If N_{ij} is the amount of nutrient i obtained from 1 kilogram of the edible portion of food j, R_i is the recommended allowance of nutrient i, and m is the number of all nutrients considered, then according to Christensen's method:

. . . .

9. M. C. Cooper and W. J. Spillman, *Human Food from an Acre of Staple Farm Products*, Farmers' Bulletin 877.

10. L. D. Stamp, "The Measurement of Land Resources," *Geographical Review* 48 (1958): 1-15.

11. R. P. Christensen, *Using Resources to Meet Food Needs*.

$$C_j = \frac{1}{m} \sum_{i=1}^{m} \frac{N_{ij}}{R_i}$$

where C_j = the total nutritional value of 1 kilogram of the edible portion of food j

$j = 1, \ldots, q.$

To get the total nutritional value of food j as purchased, multiply C_j by E_j, where E_j is the edible proportion of food j as sold at the retail level. Christensen applied this measurement to find the productivity of the resources employed in the production of different foods in terms of his nutritional unit.[12] He used the same method to find the productivity of the same resources when he revised and expanded his report in 1948.[13]

In 1944, Mighell and Christensen,[14] after proposing Christensen's same measure,[15] presented some estimates of so-called "marginal food values" that would take into account nutritional needs, consumer preferences, and production possibilities.[16] They only presented these estimates for eight foods,[17] and the source of their values is not clear.[18]

Both Black and Kiefer[19, 20] used a combination of the conventional and Christensen's first methods to obtain the productivity of land used in the production of different foods. They employed the conventional method to obtain the productivity of land in terms of calories and protein separately. Utilizing Christensen's method they formed two general groups: vitamins (vitamin A, C, thiamin, riboflavin, and niacin) and minerals (calcium, phosphorus, and iron). Finally, they calculated land productivity in terms of these two general groups.

. . . .

12. Ibid., p. 71.
13. R. P. Christensen, *Efficient Use of Land Resources in the United States*, Tables 20-37.
14. R. L. Mighell and R. P. Christensen, "Measuring Maximum Contributions to Food Needs by Producing Areas," *Journal of Farm Economics* 26 (1944): 181-95.
15. Ibid., p. 182.
16. Ibid., pp. 187-9, describes "marginal food values."
17. Ibid., p. 189.
18. Ibid., pp. 193-4.
19. J. D. Black, *Food Enough*, Chap. 12.
20. J. D. Black and M. E. Kiefer, *Future Food and Agriculture Policy*, Chap. 14.

Zobler[21] presented a method in 1961 that is similar to Christensen's except that he did not divide the sum of the nutritional relatives by the number of essential nutrients considered.

If N_{ij} is the amount of nutrient i obtained from a kilogram of the edible portion of food j, and R_i is the recommended allowance of nutrient i, then according to Zobler:

$$Z_j = \sum_{i=1}^{m} \frac{N_{ij}}{R_i}$$

where Z_j = the nutritional contribution of 1 kilogram of the edible
                  portion of food j
        $j = 1, \ldots, q$.

To allow comparison between foods, Zobler suggested a standard food that would have Z_j equal to m and would supply each nutrient in the amount of the recommended allowance ($N_{is} = R_i$, for all $i = 1, \ldots, m$, where s stands for the standard food).

Using his measure, Zobler found that 1 hectare of land in Japan is 7.7 times more efficient than in the United States, when employed for food production.[22] Zobler also computed the nutritional needs of both countries, based on their populations and the recommended allowances of each essential nutrient. But land is so much more abundant in the United States than in Japan that when Zobler took the nutritional needs into account, food production in the United States satisfied all essential needs except the riboflavin need, while only the ascorbic acid need was satisfied in Japan.[23]

Although Zobler considered all essential nutrients of a food in his method, it is possible that some nutrients are more important than others in a particular situation. For example, if the Japanese government wants to import foods to improve the nutritional intake of the Japanese population, using Zobler's method to choose the imported food might result in a very small or even zero improvement in the nutritional status, in relation to the recommended allowances, be-
. . . .

21. L. Zobler, "A New Measure of Food Production Efficiency," *Geographical Review* 51 (1961): pp. 549-69.
22. Ibid., p. 565.
23. Ibid., p. 568.

cause his method includes ascorbic acid in the measure of the nutritional contribution of food.

Suppose that there is a food W that provides only ascorbic acid and it has an international price p_w such that using Zobler's method, the ratio $E_w Z_w / p_w$, where E_w is the proportion of food W as purchased in the international market that is edible, is the largest of all possible imported foods. Importing food W is shown to be the most economical by Zobler's method, but it would not decrease malnutrition in Japan, because ascorbic acid is not deficient and food W contains only this nutrient!

Because of the relation between Christensen's and Zobler's methods,[24] $Z_j = mC_j$, the criticism of Zobler's method also applies to Christensen's. Both methods take into account all the essential nutrients of a food, but consider all of the nutrients as having equal importance. This may lead to an uneconomical choice, as shown by the hypothetical example.

Christensen and later Mighell and Christensen, conscious of this weakness, suggested evaluating foods in nutritional terms, using weights for the nutrients that are based on the nutritional deficiencies:

This assumption [equal weight for each nutrient] overlooks differences between nutrients with respect to current deficiencies. Additional units of certain products may be worth more than additional units of others, although the value of each as measured by this method [equal weight for each nutrient] are the same, because they contain more of the nutrients especially short in supply.[25]

The National Research Council recommendations for the individual nutrients can be given equal or variable weights and the values obtained for the nutrients in each product added together to determine the nutrient value. . . . Adjustment in weighting can be made if desired, to allow for the relative scarcity of the nutrients.[26]

Unfortunately they made no application following this line.

. . . .

24. Zobler was cognizant of the works of Christensen (1948) and of Mighell and Christensen, because notes 1 and 7 refer to these studies. See Zobler, pp. 549 and 551.

25. Christensen, *Resources to Meet Needs*, p. 69.

26. Mighell and Christensen, *Maximum Contributions*, pp. 186-7.

It is important to note that during a period when resources in food production had to be economized because of the war effort, Cooper and Spillman in 1917, Christensen in 1943, and Mighell and Christensen in 1944 proposed to measure the nutritional contribution of food to increase the efficiency of resources employed in food production. This is quite similar to the present situation in underdeveloped countries. These countries need to utilize their factors of production as efficiently as possible to increase their rate of economic growth.

MATHEMATICAL MEASUREMENTS

Since 1947, when Dantzig developed the simplex method that gives the solution of a linear programming problem, it is possible to suggest minimum cost diets satisfying the recommended allowances of all essential nutrients without measuring the nutritional contribution of food. Cornfield[27] in 1941 and Stigler[28] in 1945 mathematically expressed the problem of obtaining the minimum cost diet satisfying the recommended allowances for the essential nutrients. V. E. Smith[29] utilized this mathematical method, presenting a bibliography on the subject and making some interesting applications of linear programming to the problem of human diets. However, this mathematical method is not feasible when the amount of resources available is less than the one required by the linear programming solution. In such case the nutritional objective must be adjusted downward, but linear programming cannot tell us how this should be done.

A measure of the nutritional contribution of food can be used whether or not resources permit the full set of nutritional requirements to be met. Furthermore, a useful measure of the nutritional contribution of food can be easily computed by desk calculator; such a measure requires neither expensive computing equipment nor personnel skilled in linear programming.

. . . .

27. The reference to Cornfield is found in Smith, *Electronic Computation,* p. 12.

28. G. J. Stigler, "The Cost of Subsistence," *Journal of Farm Economics* 27 (1945): pp. 303-14.

29. Smith, *Electronic Computation.*

2

MEASURING
Nutritive Contributions

. . . .

WHEN AN INDIVIDUAL INTAKE OF ONE OR MORE NUTRIENTS IS LOWER than the recommended levels, it is important to know the marginal contributions of different foods to improve his nutritional status in an efficient way.

Nutritionists recommend nutrient levels which they consider high enough to avoid any of the diseases caused by malnutrition. Table 1 presents one set of such allowances used by Brazilian nutritionists to evaluate actual nutrient intake. It is possible to say that the nutritional status of an individual depends on his intake of the essential nutrients, implying a function representing this nutritional status. Also, to say that one food is more nutritious than another also indicates the existence of such a function, which we will term the nutritional function.

If N_i is the quantity of nutrient i consumed by the individual (N_i I. U. of vitamin A, for example), and if R_i is the allowance recommended by nutritionists, then:

$$n_i = \frac{N_i}{R_i} (100)$$

where n_i = the amount of nutrient i consumed, expressed as a percentage of its allowance.

TABLE 2.1
Daily nutrient allowances for a forty-five-year-old male

NUTRIENT	ALLOWANCE
Calories	3000 Calories
Protein	70 grams
Calcium	0.8 grams
Iron	10 milligrams
Vitamin A	5000 International Units
Thiamin	1.5 milligrams
Niacin	15 milligrams
Riboflavin	20 milligrams
Ascorbic Acid	75 milligrams

SOURCE: National Research Council, Food and Nutrition Board, *Recommended Dietary Allowances*, National Research Council Publication No. 589 (Washington, D. C.: National Academy of Science, 1958), p. 18.

The nutritional function can be written as:

$$S = S(n_1, n_2, \ldots, n_h, n_{h+1}, \ldots, n_m)$$

where

S = the value of the nutritional function

$n_1, n_2, \ldots, n_h$ = nutrients with a deficient intake (intake smaller than the allowance — $n_i < 100$, where $i = 1, 2, \ldots, h$)

$n_{h+1}, \ldots, n_m$ = nutrients with non-deficient intake ($n_i > 100$, where $i = h+1, \ldots, m$)

m = the total number of essential nutrients.

Because the objective is to bring the nutritional intake up to the recommended levels the properties of the nutritional function are assumed to be:

$$\frac{\partial S}{\partial n_i} = 0 \text{ for } i = 1, 2, \ldots, h$$

$$\frac{\partial S}{\partial n_i} = 0 \text{ for } i = h+1, \ldots, m.$$

This means that the marginal contribution of a nutrient intake which is higher than the recommended level does not increase the value of the nutritional function and, therefore, does not improve the nutritional status of the individual. Only the marginal intake of deficient nutrients improves the nutritional status. This allows concentration of the analysis on the deficient nutrients.

The problem is to evaluate the gain in nutritional status, or the increase in the value of the nutritional function S, given by the consumption of one additional unit of food j which furnishes one or more nutrients when consumed. Assume that one unit of food j supplies N_{ij} units of nutrient i. To express both the amount of nutrient i furnished by food j and the nutritional function in the same units:

$$n_{ij} = \frac{N_{ij}}{R_i} (100)$$

where $\quad n_{ij} =$ the quantity of nutrient i in one unit of food j, expressed as a percentage of the recommended allowance, R_i

$i = 1, 2, \ldots, h.$

The consumption of additional amounts of food j changes the values of the independent variables, $n_1, n_2, \ldots, n_h$, which express the deficient nutrient intake.

If we assume the deficient nutrients form a system of coordinates, then the consumption of food j represents a movement in a certain direction, given by the relative amounts of the deficient nutrients that food j furnishes. The mathematical concept of the directional derivative can now be applied.[30] The directional derivative of the function S in the direction j is:[31]

$$V_j S = \frac{\partial S}{\partial n_1} \cos \alpha + \frac{\partial S}{\partial n_1} \cos \beta + \ldots + \frac{\partial S}{\partial n_1} \cos \eta$$

where $\quad V_j S =$ the directional derivative of S in the direction j

$\alpha, \beta, \ldots, \eta =$ the angles that the direction j makes with the axes $n_1, n_2 \ldots n_h$, respectively.

. . . .

30. I would like to thank Professor T. R. Saving, Department of Economics, Texas A & M University, for pointing out the concept of directional derivative to me.

31. See W. Kaplan, *Advanced Calculus*, pp. 107-10, for the mathematical background of the directional derivative.

The axes represent the deficient nutrient intake.

Assuming that the direction j is give by the consumption of food j, the cosines that direction j makes with the axes are:

$$\cos a = \frac{n_{ij}}{\sqrt{n_{1j}^2 + n_{2j}^2 + \ldots + n_{hj}^2}}$$

$$\cos \beta = \frac{n_{2j}}{\sqrt{n_{1j}^2 + n_{2j}^2 + \ldots + n_{hj}^2}}$$

$$\vdots$$

$$\cos \eta = \frac{n_{hj}}{\sqrt{n_{1j}^2 + n_{2j}^2 + \ldots + n_{hj}^2}}$$

The numerator of the expression for $\cos a$ is the percentage of the allowance for nutrient 1 that is provided by one unit of food j. The denominator is the distance measured in percentage points that the individual's intake moves in direction j when he consumes one unit of food.

For example, suppose that one unit of food j provides 3 percent of the allowance for nutrient 1, and 4 percent of the allowance for nutrient 2 ($n_{1j} = 3$; $n_{2j} = 4$). The consumption of one unit of food j is then represented by point F in Figure 2.1. The change in the total nutrient intake is represented by the movement from 0 to F along $0F$ (that is, in the direction j). The distance covered by this movement is 5 percentage points ($\sqrt{3^2 + 4^2}$); that is, 3 percentage points in direction n_1 and 4 percentage points in direction n_2.

Substituting the expressions described above for the cosines in the definition of $V_j S$, the directional derivative, we obtain:

$$V_j S = \frac{\dfrac{\partial S}{\partial n_1} n_{1j} + \dfrac{\delta S}{\partial n_2} n_{2j} + \ldots + \dfrac{\partial S}{\partial n_h} n_{hj}}{\sqrt{n_{1j}^2 + n_{2j}^2 + \ldots + n_{hj}^2}}$$

The directional derivative measures the *rate* of change of the nutritional function per unit of movement as one's intake moves in di-

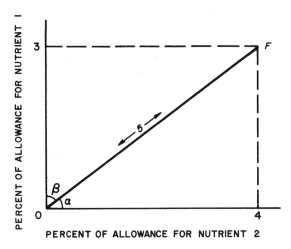

FIGURE 2.1
Change in Nutrient Intake From Food Consumption

rection *j*. The nutrient composition of food *j* determines the direction *j*, and conversely, direction *j* depends upon the proportion in which the nutrients are furnished by food *j*.

The measure of the nutritional contributions of food *j* should evaluate the amount of change in the nutritional function associated with moving in direction *j* a distance that corresponds to the consumption of food *j*. The product of the directional derivative and the square root in the denominator of V_jS provides this:

$$F_j = \left(\sqrt{n_{1j}^2 + n_{2j}^2 + \ldots + n_{hj}^2} \right) V_j S$$

$$F_j = \frac{\partial S}{\partial n_1} n_{1j} + \frac{\partial S}{\partial n_2} n_{2j} + \ldots + \frac{\partial S}{\partial n_h} n_{hj} = \sum_{i=1}^{h} \frac{\partial S}{\partial n_i} n_{ij}$$

where F_j = the nutritional contribution of one unit of food *j*.

The partial derivatives $\frac{\partial S}{\partial n_i}$, $i = 1, 2, \ldots, h$, represent weights attached to each nutrient. These weights must express the need for each nutrient in a particular situation and must also be approved by nutritionists.

NUTRITIONAL CONSIDERATIONS

Assuming that all nutrients are equally important, that is, that no nutrient is intrinsically more essential than any other, a set of weights that would express that need for each nutrient in a particular situation can be developed by taking the amount of the deficiency of each nutrient as its weight. The smaller the intake of a nutrient relative to its allowance, the larger the need to get additional amounts of this nutrient to be healthy. The larger the deficiency, the larger the weight given to the nutrient, indicating a greater need to obtain the nutrient.

Because the measure of the nutritional contribution of a food must be additive, the nutritional deficiencies are measured as percentages of the allowances, as has been done for the amounts of the deficient nutrients that one unit of the food furnishes.

Nutritionists affirm that the larger the deficiency in the intake of a nutrient with respect to its allowance, the larger the need to consume additional amounts of this nutrient, with the precaution that the nutritional allowances include amounts added for security against underestimates of either needs or actual intake levels. Therefore, the allowances do not represent *minimum* nutrient requirements. Nutritionists also feel the deficiency amounts are appropriate for the nutrients when evaluating the nutritional contribution of food. Using the amounts of the deficiencies as weights, the nutritional contribution of one unit of food j is:

$$F_j = (100 - n_1)n_{1j} + (100 - n_2)n_{2j} + \ldots + (100 - n_h)n_{hj}$$

where $(100 - n_i)$, $i = 1, 2, \ldots, h =$ the amount of the deficiency in the intake of nutrient i, expressed as a percentage of the allowance for nutrient i.

As a proposed measure of a food's nutritional contribution, this formula assumes that all nutrients have the same intrinsic importance, and the magnitudes of the deficiencies give the weights attached to the nutrients. This means that increasing the intake of one deficient nutrient by 1 percent of its allowance is as beneficial as increasing the intake of another deficient nutrient in an amount given by the ratio of the deficiency of the first to the deficiency of the other nutrient. For example, if an individual's intake is deficient by 20 percent and 60 percent of the allowances of nutrients 1 and 2, respectively, then to increase the intake of nutrient 1 by 1 percent of its allowance is as good as increasing the intake of nutrient 2 by ⅓ percent of its allowance. When the weighted sums are equal for two foods, the two foods are nutritionally indifferent. This means that the consumer can substitute one food for another without changing his nutritional status. This substitution is at the margin, with the marginal rate of substitution between the two foods equal to one.

When only two nutrients are deficient, two foods containing the deficient nutrients in different proportions can make the same nutritional contribution only if the nutrient substitution that occurs when the consumer replaces one food by another is in inverse proportion to the deficiencies. Such a replacement would leave the nutritional function unchanged because the weighted gain in nutrient 1 balances the weighted loss of nutrient 2; a three-unit gain in nutrient 1 can balance a one-unit loss in nutrient 2 only if a unit of nutrient 2 is regarded as three times as important as one unit of nutrient 1. The proportion in which the changes in the intake of nutrients 1 and 2 is equal to the ratio: deficiency of nutrient 2/deficiency of nutrient 1.

Suppose the intake of a consumer is deficient by 20 percent and by 60 percent, respectively, of the allowances of nutrients 1 and 2. Assume that one unit of a food supplies 5 percent and 2 percent of the allowances of nutrients 1 and 2, respectively. By the proposed measure, the consumer would be indifferent to a choice between this unit and one unit of another food that supplies 8 percent and 1 percent of nutrients 1 and 2, respectively. The deficiency-weighted sums of the two foods are equal to 220. Replacing the former food by the latter would increase the intake of nutrient 1 by three units and decrease nutrient 2 intake by one unit. The proportion 3/1 is equal to the ratio of the deficiencies of nutrient 2 to nutrient 1: 60/20 = 3/1.

GEOMETRICAL CONSIDERATIONS

Assuming that the choice is only between two foods and that the intake of only two nutrients is deficient, a geometrical presentation can lead to a better understanding of the problem and the suggested measure.

Suppose that n_1^o and n_2^o are the quantities of nutrients 1 and 2 consumed, expressed as percentages of their recommended allowances. This intake is deficient:

$$n_1^o, \; n_2^o < 100.$$

If the consumer spends one additional dollar on food A, he obtains A_1 and A_2 amounts of nutrients 1 and 2, respectively. If he spends the dollar on food B, he gets B_1 and B_2 units of nutrients 1 and 2. These quantities can be written as percentages of their allowances by:

$$a_1 = \frac{A_1}{R_1}(100), \; b_1 = \frac{B_1}{R_1}(100), \; a_2 = \frac{A_2}{R_2}(100) \text{ and } b_2 = \frac{B_2}{R_2}(100).$$

Having a measure of the nutritional contribution of the nutritional contribution of food, it is possible to choose between foods A and B so that the consumer gets the largest improvement in his nutritional status from the expenditure of one dollar.

In Figure 2.2, n^o represents the initial intake of nutrients 1 and 2, n_1^o and n_2^o. If the expenditure of the additional dollar is on food A, this brings the intake of nutrients 1 and 2 to n_1^a and n_2^a. If the expenditure is on food B, this brings the intake to n_1^b and n_2^b. The point at which the intake of nutrients 1 and 2 is equal to their recommended allowances is n^r.

The nutritional contributions of foods A and B, according to the suggested measure (the sums of the nutrients weighted by their deficiencies) are:

$$F_a = (100 - n_1^o)a_1 + (100 - n_2^o)a_2 = (100 - n_1^o)\left(a_1 + \frac{100 - n_2^o}{100 - n_1^o}a_2\right)$$

$$F_b = (100 - n_1^o)b_1 + (100 - n_2^o)b_2 = (100 - n_1^o)\left(b_1 + \frac{100 - n_2^o}{100 - n_1^o}b_2\right)$$

According to the proposed measure, an exchange of nutrient 1 for nutrient 2 leaves the nutritional function unchanged if the ratio in which the nutrients are exchanged (y_1/y_2) equals the inverse ratio of the deficiencies $(100 - n_2^o/100 - n_1^o)$ as shown. If:

$$\frac{y_1}{y_2} = \frac{100 - n_2^o}{100 - n_1^o}$$

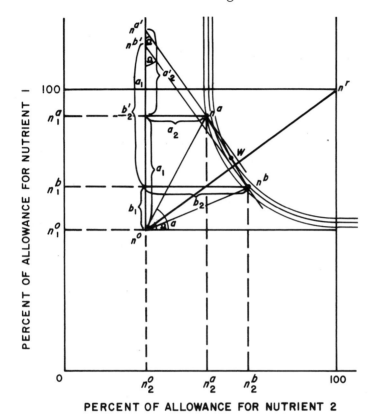

PERCENT OF ALLOWANCE FOR NUTRIENT 2

FIGURE 2.2
Sum of Nutrients, Weighted by Deficiency Levels

then

$$y_1 = \frac{100 - n_2^o}{100 - n_1^o} y_2$$

Therefore, the nutritional significance of the nutrient 2 components of foods A and B can be expressed as:

$$\frac{100 - n_2^o}{100 - n_1^o} a_2 = a_2' \qquad \text{and} \qquad \frac{100 - n_2^o}{100 - n_1^o} b_2 = b_2'$$

using nutrient 1 as the basis of reference. Now:

$$F_a = (100 - n_1^o)(a_1 + a_2')$$
$$F_b = (100 - n_2^o)(b_1 + b_2')$$

For geometrical analysis, it is convenient to find a method to determine a_2' and b_2'. This is possible because:

$$\frac{100 - n_2^o}{100 - n_1^o} = \tan \Omega$$

where $\Omega =$ the angle that the line $n^o n^r$ makes with the horizontal line through n^o.

For convenience, the line $n^o n^r$ can be called the *deficiency line*.

If straight lines are drawn through n^a and n^b perpendicular to the deficiency line, these perpendicular lines will make the angle Ω with the vertical line passing through n^o at $n^{a'}$ and $n^{b'}$. This gives two right triangles whose hypotenuses are $n^a n^{a'}$ and $n^b n^{b'}$, respectively. From Figure 2.2 it is known that a_2 and b_2 are sides of the triangles, and from trigonometry:

$$a_2 \tan \Omega = \frac{100 - n_2^o}{100 - n_1^o} \quad a_2 = a_2'$$

$$b_2 \tan \Omega = \frac{100 - n_2^o}{100 - n_1^o} \quad b_2 = b_2'$$

From Figure 2.2. it is clear that:

$$a_1 + a_2' = \left| n^{a'} - n^o \right|$$

$$b_1 + b_2' = \left| n^{b'} - n^o \right|$$

where $\left| n^{a'} - n^o \right|$ and $\left| n^{b'} - n^o \right| =$ the distance from n^o to n^{a1} and n^{b1}, respectively.

Hence:

$$F_a = (100 - n_1^o) \left| n^{a'} - n^o \right|$$

$$F_b = (100 - n_1^o) \left| n^{b'} - n^o \right|$$

The food j for which F_j (or $\left| n^{j'} - n^o \right|$) is the largest is the one with the largest nutritional contribution. Alternatively, of the lines making an angle Ω with the vertical line drawn through n^o, the line that is nearest to n^r identifies the food with the largest nutritional contribution as measured by the deficiency-weighted sum of the nutrients it supplies. The consumer will be indifferent to spending one dollar on food A or any other food that would bring his intake of the two nutrients to the straight line passing through n^a making an angle Ω with the vertical line through n^o.

Note that when the original intake of the nutrients changes, the ratio of the deficiencies may change, hence, the order of the nutritional contributions of the foods may be altered.

ANALYTICAL CONSIDERATIONS

The change in the consumer's nutritional status, when the deficiency-weighted sum of the nutrients that a food furnishes is the measure of nutritional change and only two nutrients are deficient, is given by:

$$dS = (100 - n_1)dn_1 + (100 - n_2)dn_2$$

where dS, dn_1 and dn_2 = the changes in the value of the nutritional function, and the changes in the intake of nutrients 1 and 2.

The solution of this differential equation is:

$$S = 100n_1 - \tfrac{1}{2}n_1^2 + 100n_2 - \tfrac{1}{2}n_2^2 + C$$

where C is a constant of integration. If:

$$C = (m - 2)\,5000$$

where m = the total number of essential nutrients
5000 = the value of an S intake equal to or larger than the 100 percent of the recommended allowance for a single nutrient ($100 \times 100 - \tfrac{1}{2}100^2 = 5000$),

then C represents the value that the consumer gives to the aggregate intake of non-deficient nutrients:

$$S = 100n_1 - \tfrac{1}{2}n_1^2 + 100n_2 - \tfrac{1}{2}n_2^2 + (m-2)\ 5000$$

Generalizing this result for h deficient nutrients:

$$S = (100n_1 - \tfrac{1}{2}n_1^2) + (100n_2 - \tfrac{1}{2}n_2^2) + \ldots$$
$$+ (100n_h - \tfrac{1}{2}n_h^2) + (m-h)5000 \qquad (\text{I})$$

The amount of a nutrient in each food consumed and the quantity of this food give the intake of the nutrient:

$$n_1 = \sum_{j=1}^{q} n_{1j}x_j,\ n_2 = \sum_{j=1}^{q} n_{2j}x_j,\ \ldots,\ n_h = \sum_{j=1}^{q} n_{hj}x_j$$

where $q =$ the number of foods consumed
  $x_j =$ the quantity of food j consumed.

The ratio between the increase in the value of the nutritional function (I) and an infinitesimal increase in the consumption of food j is the partial derivative of S with respect to x_j:

$$\frac{\partial S}{\partial x_j} = (100 - n_1)n_{1j} + (100 - n_2)n_{2j} + \ldots + (100 - n_h)n_{hj}$$

This is equal to the weighted sum of the nutrients supplied by one unit of food j, when the weights are the deficiencies. Using this weighted sum as the criterion, max. $\dfrac{\partial S}{\partial x_j}$ gives the food with the largest nutritional contribution, the food which the consumer should choose if he wants to improve his nutritional status as much as possible.

OTHER CONSIDERATIONS

When there are only two deficiencies in nutrient intake, the nutritional function gives iso-nutrition curves equivalent to indifference curves which are circles with their centers at the point where the intake of the deficient nutrients equals their recommended allowances (n^r in Figure 2.2). If R is the radius of the circle, then:

$$R^2 = (100 - n_1)^2 + (100 - n_2)^2$$

$$= 20000 \bullet 200n_1 + n_1^2 - 200n_2 + n_2^2$$

$$10000 - \frac{R^2}{2} = 100n_1 - \tfrac{1}{2}n_1^2 + 100n_2 - \tfrac{1}{2}n_2^2$$

$$= S - (m - 2)5000$$

$$S = 5000m - \frac{R^2}{2}$$

Therefore the smaller R is, indicating that the circle is closer to the center, the larger the value of the nutritional function S is. Because of the property $\dfrac{\partial S}{\partial n_i} = 0_1$ when $n_i > 100$, the iso-nutrition curves are straight lines outside the square 0,100 n^r 100,0 as shown in Figure 2.2. (Any point in the quadrant northeast of n^r is equivalent to n^r, because the objective is only to eliminate the deficient intake. However, this study is not interested in the form of the iso-nutrition curves when there is no deficient intake.)

In Figure 2.2, the straight lines making an angle Ω with the vertical line drawn through n^o are perpendicular to the deficiency line. Thus, these lines are tangent to the circles representing the iso-nutrition curves at the intersections of the circles with the deficiency line, because the tangent to a circle is perpendicular to the radius of the circle. Changing the origin (n^o) of the deficiency line may change the slope of this line. If so, the lines tangent to the circles will also change.

If the tangent lines are considered linear approximations of the iso-nutrition curves, maximizing nutritional status as given by these straight lines, subject to a one dollar budget constraint, becomes equivalent to the linear programming problem:

max. $S' = (100 - n_1^o)n_1 + (100 - n_2^o)n_2 - (100 - n_1^o)e_1 - (100 - n_2^o)e_2$

subject to $\qquad\qquad\qquad n_1 = a_1x_a + b_1x_b + n_1^o$

$$n_2 = a_2x_a + b_2x_b + n_2^o$$

$$n_1 - e_1 \leqslant 100$$

$$n_2 - e_2 \leqslant 100$$

$$p_ax_a + p_bx_b \leqslant 100$$

$$n_1,\ n_2,\ e_1,\ e_2,\ x_a,\ x_b \leqslant 0.$$

where $\qquad e_1$ and $e_2 =$ excesses of nutrients 1 and 2 over 100
$\qquad\qquad x_a$ and $p_a =$ the quantity and price of food A
$\qquad\qquad x_b$ and $p_b =$ the quantity and price of food B.

In Figure 2.2, the solution of this problem is at n^a, and the consumer should spend his dollar on food A.

However, when the deficiency weights are allowed to vary continuously, the nutritional function is quadratic. This leads to iso-nutrition curves which are circles with centers at n^r, in Figure 2.2. The consumer is now faced with the following quadratic programming problem:

max. $\qquad S = 100(n_1 - e_1) - \tfrac{1}{2}(n_1 - e_1)^2 + 100(n_2 - e_2) - \tfrac{1}{2}(n_2 - e_2)^2$

subject to $\qquad\qquad\qquad n_1 = a_1x_a + b_1x_b + n_1^o$

$$n_2 = a_2x_a + b_2x_b + n_2^o$$

$$n_1 - e_1 \leqslant 100$$

$$n_2 - e_2 \leqslant 100$$

$$p_ax_a + p_bx_b \leqslant 1$$

$$n_1,\ n_2,\ e_1,\ e_2,\ x_a,\ x_b \geqslant 0.$$

In Figure 2.2, the solution of this quadratic problem is at W. The consumer should spend his dollars on foods A and B in the proportion given by W because at W he is nearer to n^r than at any other point on the line n^ab^a.

In the linear programming problem, the deficiency weights are assumed constant or invariable, while in the quadratic problem the deficiency weights are continuously varying with the current intake. However, when the original intake is allowed to move in finite steps, the linear problem can be used to find the solution to the quadratic problem.

In Figure 2.3, suppose that the consumer decides to spend his dollar in two steps of fifty cents each. By the linear programming problem, the consumer should spend his first fifty cents on food A, bringing his intake to A. This changes his intake from n^o to A. At A the deficiency line is An^r, so the linear approximations of the iso-nutrient curves are now the lines $n^a n^{a''}$ and $Zn^{b''}$. The consumer should spend the remaining fifty cents on food B, bringing his intake

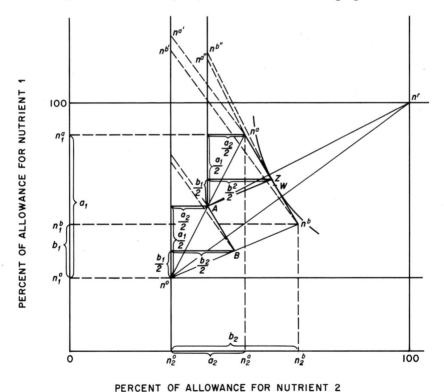

FIGURE 2.3
Selection Method For Economical Supplementary Diet

to Z. If the consumer were to spend his dollar on one food only, the solution would be n^a, as shown in Figure 2.2. The two step solution Z is closer to W, the solution where the iso-nutrition curve is tangent to the budget constraint, than the one step solution n^a. The iso-nutrition curve passing through Z is just outside the one at W, while the one at n^a is considerably removed.

Another approach to evaluating the nutritional contribution of food would be to measure the loss in an individual's work capacity caused by nutritional deficiencies. This implies a relationship between nutritional intake and the capacity to work which would make it possible to compare the net effects of the deficiency of one nutrient with that of another nutrient and give weights accordingly. This alternative is more complex and will not be treated in this study.

Any measure of the nutritional contribution of food should recognize that the consumption of certain foods can interfere with the absorption of certain nutrients by the human body. For example, spinach consumption has a negative effect on calcium utilization. On the other hand, certain nutritional allowances are related to the intake of other nutrients. For example, the allowance for thiamin can be a proportion of the caloric intake.

The generalized nutritional function can take into account the relationship between the allowance for one nutrient and the intake of another. The intake of a nutrient as a function of the consumption of all foods may not take the simple additive form as assumed earlier. To take this into account:

$$S = S(n_1, n_2, \ldots, n_m)$$

where
$$n_1 = n_1(x_1, x_2, \ldots, x_q)$$
$$n_2 = n_2(x_1, x_2, \ldots, x_q)$$
$$\cdot \qquad \cdot$$
$$\cdot \qquad \cdot$$
$$\cdot \qquad \cdot$$
$$n_m = n_m(x_1, x_2, \ldots, x_q).$$

In this case, the angles that the direction given by the consumption of one unit of food j makes with the m axes, the amounts of the m essential nutrients, are:

$$\cos a = \frac{\dfrac{\partial n_1}{\partial x_j}}{\sqrt{\left(\dfrac{\partial n_1}{\partial x_j}\right)^2 + \left(\dfrac{\partial n_2}{\partial x_j}\right)^2 + \cdots + \left(\dfrac{\partial n_m}{\partial x_j}\right)^2}}$$

$$\cos \beta = \frac{\dfrac{\partial n_2}{\partial x_j}}{\sqrt{\left(\dfrac{\partial n_1}{\partial x_j}\right)^2 + \left(\dfrac{\partial n_2}{\partial x_j}\right)^2 + \cdots + \left(\dfrac{\partial n_m}{\partial x_j}\right)^2}}$$

$$\vdots \qquad\qquad \vdots$$

$$\cos \zeta = \frac{\dfrac{\partial n_m}{\partial x_j}}{\sqrt{\left(\dfrac{\partial n_1}{\partial x_j}\right)^2 + \left(\dfrac{\partial n_2}{\partial x_j}\right)^2 + \cdots + \left(\dfrac{\partial n_m}{\partial x_j}\right)^2}}$$

The directional derivative of the general nutritional function, in the direction given by the consumption of food *j*, now becomes:

$$V_jS = \frac{\left(\dfrac{\partial S}{\partial n_1}\right)\left(\dfrac{\partial n_1}{\partial x_j}\right) + \left(\dfrac{\partial S}{\partial n_2}\right)\left(\dfrac{\partial n_2}{\partial x_j}\right) + \cdots + \left(\dfrac{\partial S}{\partial n_m}\right)\left(\dfrac{\partial n_m}{\partial x_j}\right)}{\sqrt{\left(\dfrac{\partial n_1}{\partial x_j}\right)^2 + \left(\dfrac{\partial n_2}{\partial x_j}\right)^2 + \cdots + \left(\dfrac{\partial n_m}{\partial x_j}\right)^2}}$$

This shows the rate at which the value of the nutritional function changes for unit movement in direction *j*. The amount of change in the value of the nutritional function over a distance that represents the consumption of one unit of food *j* is:

$$F_j = \left(\sqrt{\left(\dfrac{\partial n_1}{\partial x_j}\right)^2 + \left(\dfrac{\partial n_2}{\partial x_j}\right)^2 + \cdots + \left(\dfrac{\partial n_m}{\partial x_j}\right)^2}\right) V_jS$$

$$= \left(\dfrac{\partial S}{\partial n_1}\right)\left(\dfrac{\partial n_1}{\partial x_j}\right) + \left(\dfrac{\partial S}{\partial n_2}\right)\left(\dfrac{\partial n_2}{\partial x_j}\right) + \cdots + \left(\dfrac{\partial S}{\partial n_m}\right)\left(\dfrac{\partial n_m}{\partial x_j}\right)$$

This is the generalized measure of the nutritional contribution of food, when it takes any possible relationship among the food consumption and nutrient intakes into account and it considers relationships among the different nutrient intakes.

3

RECENT DEVELOPMENTS

. . . .

In 1960[32] and in 1964[33] V. E. Smith presented a new development in consumption theory, basing his studies on the application of
linear programming to human diets. Using the same tools, Lancaster[34] in 1966, made a theoretical investigation of consumer behavior.
These studies can be related to the nutritional function proposed in
the previous chapter.

V. E. Smith

Basing the presentation on his 1964 study[35], Smith says that the
conventional economic theory assumes that the utility obtained by a
household depends upon the amounts of commodities consumed. If
U^* is the index of utility and $x_1, \ldots, x_j, \ldots, x_q$ are the quantities of commodities $1 \ldots j \ldots q$ consumed by the household, then:

$$U^* = U^*(x_1 \ldots x_j \ldots x_q)$$

. . . .

32. V. E. Smith, "Measurement of Product Attributes Recognized by Consumers," in *Seminar on Consumer Preferences and Market Development for Farm
Products*, CAEA Report 5, pp. 1-27.

33. Smith, *Electronic Computation.*

34. K. J. Lancaster, "A New Approach to Consumer Theory," *Journal of
Political Economy* 74 (1966): pp. 132-57.

35. Smith, *Electronic Computation*, pp. 136-43.

With the budget constraint this is the conventional treatment of consumption theory using indifference curves.

In his new approach, Smith considers consumption goods as "bundles of separate goal-satisfying attributes."[36] The measure of utility U then becomes a single-valued function of the levels of attainment of a particular set of objectives:

$$U = f(b_1 \ldots b_i \ldots b_m)$$

where $b_i =$ the level of attainment of the individual's i goal.[37]

The levels of the attributes depend upon the quantities of commodities consumed:

$$b_i = g_i(x_1 \ldots x_j \ldots x_q)$$

Substituting the second equation into the first he gets the traditional utility function:

$$U = w(x_1 \ldots x_j \ldots x_q)$$

If a certain utility level, $U = U_k$ where $U_k = f(b_1^k \ldots b_j^k \ldots b_m^k)$, is specified in the first equation, the b_i variables become constant. "Each such set of b_i corresponds to a particular level of utility. Several such sets may correspond to the same utility level. If b_i^k, for instance, provides satiation of the ith goal, increases in its value will not alter the utility level as long as over-attainment involves no loss of satisfactions."[38]

The problem is to economize within the indifference region where $U = U_k$:[39]

The diet problem in linear programming is exactly this kind of analysis of the problem of minimizing the cost of attaining specified levels of the various objectives, that is, a specified level of preference. Consider a case in which there are two commodities and three nutritional goals to be attained at specified levels. In Figure [3.1],

· · · · · · · ·

36. *Ibid.*, p. 137.
37. *Ibid.*, p. 139.
38. *Ibid.*, p. 139.
39. *Ibid.*, pp. 140-1.

OA *represents the quantity of commodity I needed if the specific caloric level is to be attained by the consumption of I alone: OB is the quantity of commodity II required for this purpose if only II is to be consumed. If less of I is taken, the deficiency in calories may be made up by adding II, at a constant rate determined by the ratio of the caloric content of commodity II to that of commodity I. The slope of the line AB measures the substitution ratio. Any combination of foods I and II plotted along line AB will satisfy the caloric requirement. Similarly, the thiamin level desired (b_2^k) can be attained by any combination of foods along line CD, and the riboflavin level (b_3^k) by any combination of foods along line EF.*

If the utility obtained from one nutritional element is independent of the quantities of the other elements present, any point along AB represents a given level of utility obtained from calories, any point

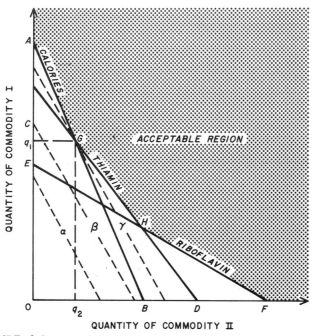

FIGURE 3.1
Linear Programming Analysis

From: Victor E. Smith, *Electronic Computation of Human Diets,* p. 141.

along CD *represents a given level of utility from thiamin, and any point along* EF *represents a given level of utility from riboflavin. The conventional programming requirement that each of these three levels can be equalled or exceeded rules out any possibility of substituting one goal for another — that is, of replacing deficiencies in one nutrient by excesses of another. Thus the only acceptable points taking all three goals into account, are those on or above* AGHF, *in the shaded region. Any such point provides a level of utility at least equal to* $U_k = U(b_1^k) + U(b_2^k) + U(b_3^k)$. *The combinations of foods along* AG *provide thiamin and riboflavin in excess of the* b_i^k *levels, but the conventional linear programming procedure regards any such excesses as irrelevant (possessing zero marginal utilities). Thus curve* AGHF *can be regarded as the lower boundary of an indifferent region within which any combination of commodities is an equally satisfactory means of attaining the specific* b_i^k *levels of these goals.*

The programming problem is to choose the acceptable commodity set which requires the least expenditure. For positive prices of both commodities, the least-cost combination must lie on the curve AGHF, *for all other acceptable points involve larger quantities of at least one commodity. The dotted lines* α, β, *and* γ *in Figure [3.1] show the combinations of commodities I and II which can be purchased for dollar expenditures of* α, β, *and* γ, *respectively. It is obvious to the eye that* 0_{q1} *of commodity I and* 0_{q2} *of commodity II constitute the least-cost combination. Changes in the prices of the foods by changing the slopes of* α, β, *and* γ, *may alter the optimal combinations of foods.*

In more recent work (unpublished), Smith uses linear programming to find the least-cost diet that supplements the deficient nutritional intake of Colombian families (the right-hand values of the constraints of the least-cost diet are the amounts of the deficiencies). Nevertheless, he assumes that the families can afford the added expenditure, and this may not necessarily be true.

K. LANCASTER

In 1966, Lancaster proposed a similar analytical apparatus to explain consumer behavior. In Lancaster's "simplified model,"[40] the consumer tries to maximize a utility index that is a function of the

. . . .

40. Lancaster, "New Approach," p. 136.

characteristics of commodities, subject to certain constraints. Lancaster's commodity characteristics are equivalent to Smith's attributes of consumer goods. Lancaster's theory states:

$$\begin{array}{ll} \text{max.} & U\ (z) \\ \text{subject to} & px \leqslant k \\ \text{with} & z = Bx \\ \text{and} & z,\ x \geqslant 0 \end{array}$$

where $U\ (z) =$ the utility index as a function of the characteristics

$z = (z_1 \ldots z_i \ldots z_m)$ is a vector that shows the amounts of characteristics consumed

$z_i =$ the b_i in Smith's notation

$p = (p_1 \ldots p_j \ldots p_q)$ is a vector with the prices of the q commodities

$B =$ the matrix that presents the "consumption technology," such that any element b_{ij} represents the amount of characteristic i in one unity of commodity j.

For this study, only foods enter into the list of consumption goods, and only deficient nutrients enter into the list of characteristics provided by the foods. This means that:

$$b_{ij} = n_{ij}$$

where $n_{ij} =$ the amount of nutrient i in one unit of food j expressed as a percentage of the recommended allowance.

As a matter of fact, the number of foods is larger than the number of nutrients for which nutritionists suggest allowances. This means that q is larger than h, the number of deficient nutrients. In Lancaster's analysis:[41]

Here, the consumption technology, z = Bx, *has fewer equations than variables so that, for every characteristics vector there is more than one goods vector. For every point in his characteristics-space,*
. . . .

41. *Ibid.,* pp. 139-40.

the consumer has a choice between different goods vectors. Given a price vector, this choice is a pure efficiency choice, so that for every characteristics vector the consumer will choose the most efficient combination of goods to achieve that collection of characteristics, and the efficiency criterion will be minimum cost.

The efficiency choice for a characteristics vector z^* will be the solution of the canonical linear program

$$\begin{aligned} &\text{Minimize} && \text{px} \\ &\text{subject to} && \text{Bx} = z^* \\ &&& \text{x} \geqslant 0 \end{aligned}$$

Since this is a linear program, once we have the solution x^* for some z^* with value k^*, we can apply a scalar multiple to fit the solution to any budget value k and characteristics vector $(k/k^*)z^*$. By varying z^*, the consumer, given a budget constraint $px = k$, can determine a characteristics frontier consisting of all z such that the value of the above program is just equal to k. There will be a determinate goods vector associated with each point of the characteristics frontier.

In Figure 3.2, the efficiency frontier obtained by the consumer who has one dollar to spend on commodities A, B, and C is shown. The three commodities supply him with two characteristics in different proportions as shown by lines $0a$, $0b$, and $0c$. Points a, b, and c are given by the levels of characteristics 1 and 2 that he can get if he spends his dollar on either A or B or C. The lines ab and bc show the amounts of characteristics 1 and 2 that he can get if he spends his dollar on various combinations of commodities A and B, or B and C. Any combination of commodities A and C given on the line ac is dominated by some other combination. This means that the consumer can get the same amounts of characteristics 1 and 2 by combining commodities A and B, or B and C, or B alone, while spending a smaller amount of money. Thus, the efficiency frontier is $0abc0$.

Usually it is possible to obtain a more economical solution for the linear programming problem above when inequalities are used instead of equalities making $Bx \geqslant z^*$. With the inequalities, the consumer can obtain a combination of characteristics such that at least one characteristic is exactly achieved and all others are provided in excess. In Figure 3.2, the point F now can be achieved by buying

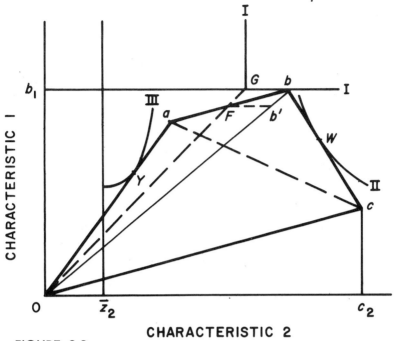

FIGURE 3.2
Lancaster's Model

only $0b'$ of commodity B. Characteristic 1 is supplied in the exact amount demanded, while characteristic 2 has an excess equal to Fb'. If the consumer buys only $0b'$ of commodity B he spends less than one dollar. If he buys commodities A and B in the proportions that give him exactly F, he must spend the whole dollar. When excesses are permitted, then, the equivalent of any combination that includes food A can be achieved more cheaply by buying only commodity B.

Suppose the consumer wants to spend a maximum of one dollar. Because of the inequalities $Bx \geqslant z^*$, that allow the consumer to have excesses, he can reach points that he could not attain when equalities were used. Points in the area $0abb_10$ can be reached by buying commodity B which gives an excess of characteristic 2. For example, the consumer can reach G by spending one dollar on commodity B ($0b$). He gets the exact amount of characteristic I demanded and an excess equal to Gb of characteristic 2. Points in the area $0cc_20$ can be attained by buying commodity C, which provides an excess of characteristic 1. Thus the efficiency frontier is expanded to $0b_1bcc_20$.

Using a linear programming problem in which $Bx \geqslant z^*$ implies the existence of a special indifference curve in which the marginal utilities of excesses are equal to zero. In Figure 3.2, suppose the consumer wants to obtain the characteristics in the proportion given at F, while spending exactly one dollar. Then he can attain the point G by buying $0b$ of commodity B that gives him an excess of characteristic 2 equal to Gb. As excesses of characteristics have zero marginal utility, the indifference curve is the right angle curve I, passing through G. An excess of any one of the characteristics does not put the consumer on a different indifference curve.

The decision that the marginal utility of any excess is equal to zero is a subjective decision that must be made by the consumer. Lancaster uses the efficiency frontier derived from the equalities, $Bx = z^*$, because he wants to separate the objective problem of finding the efficiency frontier from the subjective problem of choosing a point on the efficiency frontier. That is, he does not want to make any assumption concerning the form of the indifference curve.[42]

A consumer's complete choice subject to a budget contraint px $\leqslant$ k *can be considered as consisting of two parts:*
a) An efficiency choice, determining the characteristics frontier and the associated efficient goods collection.
b) A private choice, determining which point on the characteristics frontier is preferred by him.

In Figure 3.2, Lancaster's efficiency choices for a maximum expenditure of one dollar are shown on the line $0abc0$. The private choice will be determined by the consumer. If his indifference curve is II, he chooses W.

Earlier, Smith developed a similar procedure:[43]

Although the programming procedure itself does not provide for comparisons among goals, an experiment can be devised that will accomplish this. Compute minimum cost diets for a comprehensive group of alternative sets of goal attainment levels [characteristics
· · · · · · · ·

42. *Ibid.*, p. 139.
43. Smith, *Electronic Computation*, pp. 141-2.

levels] and ask a consumer to choose among these diets, telling him what the cost of each diet will be. When the marginal cost of raising an attainment level [characteristic level] is positive, choice among diets involving different sets of attainment levels [characteristics levels] may involve changes in his expenditure. The diet he chooses will embody that set of attainment levels [characteristics levels] which he finds just worth the extra expenditure.

Once the subjective choice is regarded as a choice among characteristics rather than among commodities, a new problem arises. Because characteristics are provided in fixed proportions, it may happen that one characteristic has a negative marginal utility. In Figure 3.2, let the consumer desire to acquire $0\bar{z}_2$ of characteristic 2. Beyond this amount the marginal utility of characteristic 2 becomes negative. The consumer has a positive marginal utility for characteristic 1. His indifference curve looks like III. Commodities A, B, and C furnish characteristics 1 and 2 in fixed proportions given by lines $0a$, $0b$, and $0c$, respectively. The consumer maximizes his utility at Y, buying only $0Y$ of commodity A. Substituting vitamin A and calories for characteristics 1 and 2 and foods for commodities, this is the behavior of a consumer that is on a diet to lose weight. Because of the joint supply of calories and vitamin A, if vitamin A has a positive marginal utility, he will choose an intake of calories larger than the one that would otherwise have been desired. This is so, because he has to take calories to obtain vitamin A.

PURCHASE OF NUTRITION

The problem of choosing economical foods is one in which commodities are to be chosen for their nutritional characteristics. Moreover, these characteristics are measurable, so it is a natural choice for an empirical application of Lancaster's model. The results here do not depend upon the analysis developed by Lancaster, however, as work on this study was begun prior to Lancaster's article.

The nutritional functions of Chapter 2 correspond to Lancaster's utility function $U(z)$, where the only characteristics considered are the nutritional ones. Here Lancaster's consumption technology matrix gives the amounts of the deficient nutrients in one unit of each food. Only foods appear on the commodity and in the price vectors. Lancaster's budget constraint k is the amount of money reserved for food expenditure. In the present application, there is an added constraint that determines the excesses of nutrients over the recommended allowance levels. These excesses enter in the nutritional function such that the value of the function changes as long as the intake of a nutrient is smaller than the allowance. Thus the constraint has relevance only to the subjective aspect of the problem. In Lancaster's model, the consumer wants to maximize the utility function subject to constraints. In this application the consumer wishes to maximize the nutritional function subject to constraints.

Taking nutritional function (I) and making

$$z = (z_1 \ldots z_i \ldots z_h) = (n_1 \ldots n_i \ldots n_h) = n$$
$$p = (p_1 \ldots p_j \ldots p_q)$$
$$x = (x_1 \ldots x_j \ldots x_q)$$
$$B = b_{ij} = n_{ij} = N, \text{ where } i = 1 \ldots h \text{ and } j = 1 \ldots q$$
$$e = (e_1 \ldots e_i \ldots e_h)$$
$$r = \text{an } (lxh) \text{ vector,}$$

where e = the excesses over the allowance levels
r = an (lxh) vector,

the following application of Lancaster's model can be made:

$$\text{max. } S = 100 \, (n_1 - e_1) - \tfrac{1}{2}(n_1 - e_1)^2 + \ldots$$
$$+ \; 100(n_h - e_h) - \tfrac{1}{2}(n_h - e_h)^2 + (m - h)5000 \; (I)$$

subject to
$$n = Nx$$
$$n - e \leqslant r$$
$$px \leqslant k$$
$$n, x, e \geqslant 0.$$

This is the same quadratic programming problem presented in Chapter 2.

Lancaster's theoretical analysis is designed to separate the problem of choice into its technical and subjective components by first determining an efficiency frontier that depends only on the costs of providing specified combinations of characteristics, and then allowing subjective preferences to play their part in making the choice among the various combinations of characteristics available at a given cost. The subjective portion of the problem is represented in the model by the objective function to be maximized (the utility function); the technical aspects of the problem are represented by the characteristics matrix which relates quantities of goods to the bundles of characteristics provided by them.

First calculate the efficiency frontier from the linear programming problem:

$$
\begin{aligned}
&\text{min.} && px \\
&\text{subject to } n^* = Nx \\
&&& x \geqslant 0
\end{aligned}
$$

where $n^* =$ a specified set of nutritional levels

After obtaining the cost k^* for this problem calculate n, the amount of nutrients provided in the proportions of n^*, that can be purchased by the food budget k; that is $n = (k/k^*)n^*$. This must be done for n^* ranging over all possible sets of proportions. (The restriction $n - e \leqslant r$ is ignored because it relates to the subjective aspect of this problem.) Once the efficiency frontier is obtained, find the point in this frontier that is tangent to the indifference curves given by the nutritional function (I).

This analytical procedure could also be used as a computing procedure, but would be extremely inefficient. Imagine the number of linear programming problems necessary to express all the possible intake combinations of the deficient nutrients. Of course, parametric linear programming can reduce these computations. However, for computational purposes, Lancaster would probably suggest the use of ordinary quadratic programming methods, even though these blur the distinction between technical and subjective aspects of the problem.

In Figure 3.3, a graphical analysis of Lancaster's analytical solution when there are only two foods and two deficient nutrients is presented. The amounts of nutrients are expressed as percentages of their allowances. The points n^a and n^b represent the quantities of nutrients 1 and 2 obtained by spending k dollars on either food A or food B. The efficiency frontier is on $0n$ $^an^b0$. In Chapter 2 it was pointed out that the iso-nutrition curves given by function (I) are portions of circles with their center at the point where the recommended allowances of deficient nutrients are exactly fulfilled. Therefore, the consumer maximizes his nutritional status at W, where the iso-nutrition curve I is tangent to the efficiency frontier. This is the solution of the quadratic programming problem stated above. It is also the solution approached by the method suggested in this study (see Chapter 4).

The consumer does not necessarily maximize his utility at a tangency point. He may be in a point inside the efficiency frontier. When the utility function is the nutritional function (I) the maximum nutritional status attainable is that in which the intake of all nutrients are equal to their allowances; that is n^r in Figure 3.3. Therefore, if the budget constraint were greater than the minimum cost diet that provides all the recommended allowances, a portion of the efficiency

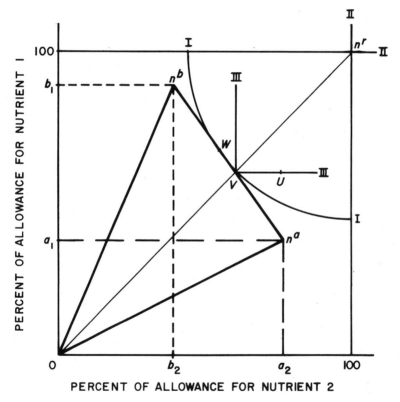

FIGURE 3.3
Purchase of Nutrition (I)

frontier is in the northeast quadrant with its origin at n^r and the consumer would choose n^r to buy the minimum cost diet obtained by the standard linear programming problem. Such a problem makes no explicit reference to a nutritional function.

The absence of an explicit nutritional function in the standard linear programming formulation of the least-cost diet problem becomes significant when the budget constraint does not allow all the deficiencies to be removed. A natural procedure derived from the standard least-cost diet approach would be to select as large a fraction of the diet at n^r as the budget allows. This solution is called the fractional least-cost diet. If the least-cost diet that provides $n^* \geqslant r$, costs t^* dollars, and the budget constraint is $t < t^*$, then the fractional least-cost diet will supply $n = (t/t^*)n^*$. The fractional least-cost diet, however, does not generally lead to the solution given by the quadratic problem above. In Figure 3.3, V is the solution obtained from the fractional least-cost diet. It is different than W.

The fractional least-cost diet leads to iso-nutrition curves that are right angle curves, with the angle on the deficiency line. These iso-nutrition curves are rather peculiar. They show that the consumer is indifferent to a choice between U and V in Figure 3.3. This means that for the same level of nutrient 1, the consumer is not better off when he has a greater amount of nutrient 2 in U than in V, although the intake of nutrient 2 is deficient. So, the fractional least-cost diet is not the best solution, if nutritional benefit can be received from an increase in the quantity of one deficient nutrient alone. On the other hand, if a nutrient can be utilized only in fixed proportions to the other nutrients, the fractional least-cost diet points to the proper solution (as long as excesses of individual nutrients have no nutritional significance).

When the solution of the quadratic programming problem presented above is such that at least one deficient nutrient is provided in excess of its allowance, this solution is also a solution of the fractional least-cost diet problem. In the fractional least-cost diet, excesses over the proportions given by the deficiency ratios do not count; in the nutritional function (I), excesses over the allowances do not influence the value of the function. The slopes of the iso-nutrition curves become the same in both problems when there is an excess over the allowance. However, it is not true that all fractional least-cost diets are solutions of the quadratic programming problem, when the solution of the latter presents at least one excess. This is illustrated in Figure 3.4.

In Figure 3.4, the Lancaster efficiency frontier is $0ABCO$. Suppose that the point where the intake is equal to the allowances is at n_1. The fractional least-cost diet solutions are the combinations of foods A and B represented by points on line AB between V_I and B. The points between V_I and B cost no more than V_I and provide the same amount of nutrient 1 and larger amounts of nutrient 2 (however, the excesses of nutrient 2 yield neither benefit nor loss). The quadratic programming solutions are the combinations between W_I and B. It is clear from Figure 3.4 that the $W_I B$ set is smaller than the $V_I B$ set. Solutions like those occur when n^r is in area I. This area is bounded by the vertical axis, line AB and the extension from B of the line $0B$.

Suppose that n^r is at n^r_{II}. The two solutions are the same: only

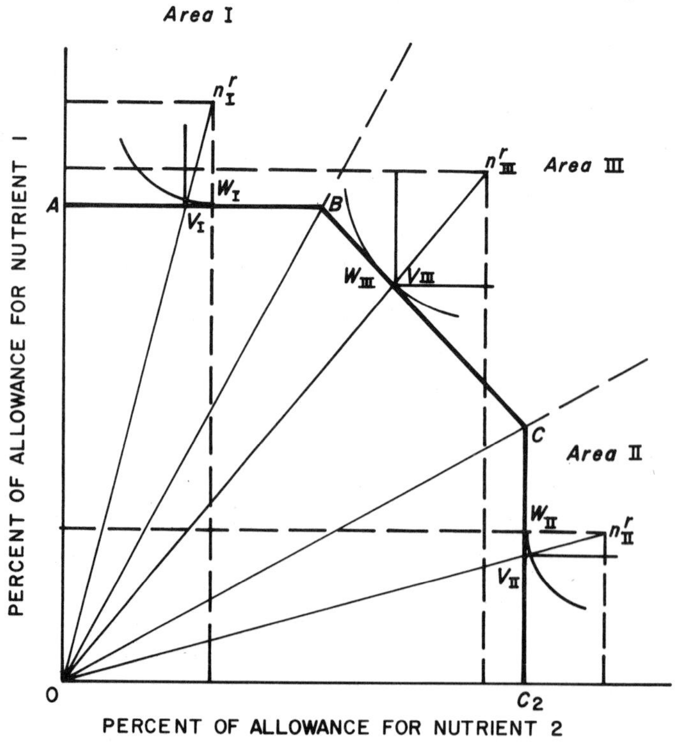

FIGURE 3.4
Purchase of Nutrition (II)

food C should be purchased. Solutions like that occur when n^r is in area II. This area is bounded by the horizontal axis, line CC_2 and the extension from C of the line $0C$.

Suppose that n^r is at n^r_{III}. This is equivalent to the solutions of Figure 3.3. The solution will generally be different. Solutions like that occur when n^r is in area III. This area is bounded by extensions from B and C of the lines $0B$ and $0C$, respectively and the line BC.

Thus the problem being studied is a natural application of Lancaster's theory, and when resources are not sufficient to buy the least-cost diet providing all the recommended allowances, a fractional least-cost diet may not be the best diet in nutritional terms.

4

NEW METHOD

and an application

. . . .

NUTRITIONISTS OF THE BRAZILIAN MINISTRY OF HEALTH SURVEYED THE
nutritional conditions of families living in four villages of the state
of Rio Grande do Norte: Santo Antônio in November, 1959;[44] Boacica
in December, 1960;[45] Currais in August, 1961;[46] and São Paulo do
Potengi in September, 1961.[47] Several families living in these four
villages were classified into four categories according to their wealth:
very poor, poor, well to do, and very well to do. However, no data
is presented indicating what amount of wealth or income places a
family in a particular category.

The nutritionists compared the actual nutritional intake, calculated
from tables of food composition, with the recommended allowances
suggested by the National Research Council of the U.S. in 1958, on

. . . .

44. National Food Commission, *Inquérito de Alimentação Realizado em Santo
Antônio, Estado de Rio Grande do Norte (Brasil).*

45. National Food Commission, *Estudo de Consumo de Alimentos e das Condições Socio-Econômicas nas Famílias Representativas do Povoado de Boacica,
Município de Touros, Rio Grande do Norte, Brasil, Novembro de 1960.*

46. National Food Commission, *Estudo da Alimentação e das Condições Econômico-Sociais Realizado no Povoado de Currais, Município de Nisia Floresta — Rio
Grande do Norte, Brasil, Agôsto de 1961.*

47. National Food Commission, *Inquérito sôbre Hábitos e Recursos Alimentares, São Paulo do Potengi, Rio Grande do Norte, Brasil.*

a per capita basis for the families sampled.[48] From these results the deficiencies of the different nutrients were obtained.

They listed the prices of some twenty foods for each village and computed the amounts of the essential nutrients that could be obtained by the expenditure of Cr $10 (ten Brazilian cruzeiros) on these foods.

A new method for finding economical supplementary diets for families with a deficient nutritional intake has been developed with rules formulated to give the basic operations of the method. There are established procedures for the computer solutions of linear and quadratic programming problems used in the method, but it is not within the scope of the present study to discuss their details.

To demonstrate how this new method can be used to obtain economical supplementary diets, it has been applied to the diets of families with deficient nutritional intake in the Northeastern region of Brazil. The existing consumption pattern of these families was assumed constant, thus only the additional consumption of foods constituted the supplementary diet. The economical supplementary diets computed by the new method were compared with the minimum cost supplementary diets calculated by linear programming.

Mainly intended for small problems, the new method needs only a desk calculator. Though the process becomes very time consuming, in poor countries or in poor regions of a country where the nutritional deficiencies are more acute and there is a lack of the computers and skilled personnel that linear programming demands, the new method becomes even more important.

SELECTION PROCEDURE

The basic selection procedure for the new method first involves the question of what food gives the largest nutritional contribution from a given unit of money spent on food.

. . . .

48. To be consistent in the Currais date, the recommended allowance of riboflavin for the poor families would have to be 3.11 milligrams per capita. This is much too large, suggesting that there was an error in the computations of this nutrient. According to the U.S. Interdepartmental Committee on Nutrition for National Development, *Northeast Brazil, Nutrition Survey, March-May 1963*, p. 288, an acceptable intake of riboflavin is between 1.2 and 1.4 milligrams per day. Because of this discrepancy, a supplementary diet was not computed for poor families of Currais.

The unit of money can only be spent on one food, and the first question is answered by using a measure of the nutritional contribution of food such as the one suggested in this study. This food is included in the supplementary diet, changing the nutritional intake, and hence the deficiencies.

The second and last step in the selection procedure is to determine if nutritional deficiencies still exist after the addition of the new food. If they do, it is necessary to answer the first question again, recomputing the nutritional contribution of food and introducing new foods into the supplementary diet until no deficiencies exist.

The selection procedure gives what is called a feasible solution in linear programming theory. In this solution, all constraints of the problem are fulfilled, but the objective function is not at the optimum. In this case, the nutritional allowances are satisfied, but not necessarily at minimum cost. The feasible solution found by using this method may be very close to the minimum cost diet, however, and in certain situations is good enough. The advantage of the method is that it does not employ matrix operations calculus that are cumbersome on a desk calculator.

Now it is possible to formulate a set of rules giving an economical supplementary diet which eliminates the nutritional deficiencies:

RULE 1. *Calculate the nutritional contribution of spending one unit of money on each food by multiplying the amount of each nutrient furnished by the food by the deficiency of that nutrient and adding these products. The amount of nutrient and the deficiency are measured as percentages of the recommended allowances. The food with the largest nutritional contribution should be introduced into the supplementary diet.*

RULE 2. *In computing the nutritional contribution, when the amount of a nutrient furnished in spending one unit of money on a food is larger than the deficiency, consider only that amount of the nutrient which is equal to the deficiency. The reason for this is that when a deficiency is eliminated its weight becomes zero.*

RULE 3. *After introducing the food with the largest nutritional contribution, recompute the deficiencies and reuse Rules 1 and 2 until all deficiencies are eliminated.*

These rules were applied to select economical supplementary diets for the families surveyed by the nutritionists of the Brazilian Ministry of Health. Because the number and the amount of deficiencies are not very large in the well-to-do and very well-to-do families, supplementary diets were only computed for the poor and very poor families studied.

The selection procedure for the new method is illustrated by showing part of the computations and the development of the supplementary diet for the very poor families of Boacica. This case is discussed because it involved the smallest number of deficient nutrients. Table 4.1 presents the beginning of the calculations. For simplicity, only the five foods that originally had the largest nutritional contributions are shown.

The first five lines of Table 4.1 give the amounts of the deficient nutrients that a consumer can obtain by spending Cr $.10 (ten Brazilian "centavos") on each of the foods shown. The next five lines present the nutrient contents as percentages of the respective recommended allowances. Lines 11 to 15 are obtained by multiplying the nutrient contents as percentages of the allowances by the deficiencies (also expressed as percentages of the allowances). These are the weighted nutrient contributions. Finally, the last line is the sum of the weighted nutrients contributions, that is, the deficiency-weighted sum of the nutrients. The food with the largest sum should be introduced in the supplementary diet.

The first step introduces Cr $.10 of sweet potato in the supplementary diet, because this food has the largest deficiency-weighted sum, at the beginning. To find the food that should be introduced by spending the next Cr $.10, recalculate lines 11 to 15 using the new deficiencies. The new deficiencies are the old ones minus the amounts of nutrients furnished by sweet potato in lines 6 to 10, respectively. Continue this process according to Rule 2 until all the deficiencies are eliminated. Note that this procedure can be easily executed on a desk calculator.

For this supplementary diet, the sequence of choice is: Cr $.50 of sweet potato, Cr $.10 of macassa beans, Cr $.10 of sweet potato, Cr $.10 of macassa beans, Cr $.20 of sweet potato, Cr $.10 of macassa beans, Cr $.20 of sweet potato, Cr $4.10 of macassa beans, Cr $.10 of sweet potato, and finally Cr $2.70 of macassa beans.

Tables 4.2, 4.3, 4.4, 4.5, 4.6, 4.7, and 4.8 present the economical diets computed by employing the rules of the selection procedure. These tables also show the minimum cost supplementary diets calculated by linear programming, using the amounts of deficiencies as the quantities of nutrients to be provided. Note that the diets selected by the new method are very similar to the diets found by linear programming (the quantities given are for weights as purchased).

For the families of São Paulo do Potengi the suggested daily consumption of sweet potato (1889 grams) seems to be too large to be acceptable (more than ten times the existing consumption).[49] Any diversification in the supplementary diet, however, would imply an increase in its cost. In this particular case, it is possible to establish a maximum acceptable level for the consumption of sweet potato. When this maximum is achieved, the selection rules choose the food with the second largest nutritional contribution. Suppose the maximum acceptable consumption of sweet potato is 1000 grams. This means that after spending Cr $5.40 on sweet potato, another food should be introduced. This food is macassa beans. The new economical diet that eliminates the deficiencies consists of 1000 grams of sweet potato at Cr $5.40 and 221 grams of macassa beans at Cr $4.90. The new diet costs Cr $10.30, a very small increase over the one that includes only sweet potato.

Only four foods — sweet potato, macassa beans, pumpkin, and fresh milk — qualified for inclusion in any of the diets. Most often the diet consisted of sweet potato plus one other food. Nutritionists would expect macassa beans or even fresh milk to be economical and might find it strange that sweet potato and pumpkin appear in all these diets. This happens because sweet potato and pumpkin are very inexpensive in these villages.

The reader should be aware that the surveys covered a period of only one week and did not take seasonal variation and quantities of foods available for consumption into account. At other times of the year, for instance, sweet potato might not be an economical food.

Because of the finite steps used in the selection procedure there are generally excesses in the amounts of all the nutrients provided by the economical supplementary diets. For the very poor families of Boacica (Table 4.2), the excess of protein is more than fifteen

· · · · · · · ·

49. National Food Commission, *Inquérito, São Paulo do Potengi*, p. 50.

times as large as the amount of its deficiency, while there is almost no excess of calcium. The *scarcest nutrient* is the one with the smallest ratio of the amount of nutrient provided by the supplementary diet to the amount of original deficiency of the same nutrient. For the very poor families of Boacica, calcium is the scarcest nutrient.

SUBSTITUTION PROCEDURE

The economical supplementary diets for the poor families of São Paulo do Potengi and for the very poor families of Currais can be made still more inexpensive by changing the proportions of the foods in these diets. The economy will not be larger than 10 percent of the minimum cost supplementary diet.

To accomplish this, it is necessary to determine whether it is possible to reduce the cost of the economical supplementary diet obtained in the selection procedure by substitution among the foods contained in this diet. To avoid a large number of computations, substitution among foods is limited to the ones in the economical supplementary diet.

When substitution is possible, it is also necessary to know how it takes place. If, by spending the same amount of money for the supplementary diet, it is possible to increase the level of the scarcest nutrient while the amounts of the other nutrients do not become smaller than their allowances, then substitution among these foods can provide the same amount of the scarcest nutrient, with a diet that is less expensive. This leads to Rule 4:

RULE 4. *When substituting one unit of a food in the supplementary diet for one unit of another food in the diet (the unit in money terms, Cr $.10 for example), see if the level of the scarcest nutrient increases while the amounts of the other nutrients do not become smaller than their recommended allowances.*

When trying to substitute Cr $.10 of macassa beans for Cr $.10 of sweet potato in the supplementary diets for Boacica (Tables 4.2 and 4.3), the calcium level increases while the level of vitamin A becomes smaller than its allowance. The amount of calcium for the

TABLE 4.1

Nutritional contribution of Cr $ .10-worth of food—very poor families of Boacica (measured by deficiency-weighted sum of nutrients)

		SWEET POTATO	MACASSA BEANS	MANGO	BANANA	FRESH MILK
Nutrient content	(1) Protein (gm.)	0.240	1.325	0.054	.131	0.17
	(2) Calcium (mg.)	6.200	8.190	1.620	1.700	5.78
	(3) Vitamin A (I.U.)	92.000	1.790	105.030	34.060	6.19
	(4) Thiamin (mg.)	0.018	0.0322	0.0054	.0052	0.0015
	(5) Riboflavin (mg.)	0.010	0.0107	0.0054	.0066	0.0083
	(6): $\dfrac{(1) \times 100}{\text{Allowance (52.2 gm.)}}$	0.46	2.54	0.10	0.25	0.33
Nutrient content: percent of per capita allowance	(7): $\dfrac{(2) \times 100}{\text{Allowance (900 mg.)}}$	0.69	0.91	0.18	0.19	0.64
	(8): $\dfrac{(3) \times 100}{\text{Allowance (3847 I.U.)}}$	2.34	0.05	2.72	0.88	0.16
	(9): $\dfrac{(4) \times 100}{\text{Allowance (.81 mg.)}}$	2.22	3.98	0.67	0.64	0.19
	(10): $\dfrac{(5) \times 100}{\text{Allowance (1.31 mg.)}}$	0.76	0.82	0.41	0.50	0.63
Weighted nutrient contribution	(11): (6) × Deficiency (12%)	6	30	1	3	4
	(12): (7) × Deficiency (72%)	50	66	13	14	46
	(13): (8) × Deficiency (28%)	66	1	76	25	4
	(14): (9) × Deficiency (5%)	11	20	3	3	1
	(15): (10) × Deficiency (55%)	41	45	23	28	35
Total nutritional contribution	(16): (11) + (12) + (13) + (14) + (15)	174	162	116	73	90

SOURCE: National Food Commission, *Estudo de Consumo de Alimentos . . . Boacica*, Tables 44, 45, and 46.

TABLE 4.2

Daily supplementary diet — very poor families of Boacica
(per capita)

FOOD	QUANTITY	COST (CR $)

I — Economical supplementary diet (E.S. Diet) by new method*
   (selection procedure only)

FOOD	QUANTITY	COST (CR $)
Sweet potato	220 grams	$1.10
Macassa beans	424 grams	$7.10
		total $8.20

II — Minimum cost supplementary diet (M.C.S. Diet) by linear
   programming

FOOD	QUANTITY	COST (CR $)
Sweet potato	206 grams	$1.032
Macassa beans	426 grams	$7.131
		total $8.163

III — Nutritional data

DEFICIENT NUTRIENTS	ALLOWANCE	DEFICIENCY	PROVIDED BY E.S. DIET	PERCENT OF ALLOWANCE	
				Deficiency	Provided by E.S. Diet
Protein (gm.)	52.20	6.30	96.715	12	185
Calcium (mg.)	900.00	648.00	649.690†	72	72
Vitamin A (I. U.)	3847.00	1077.00	1139.900	28	29
Thiamin (mg.)	0.81	0.04	2.4842	5	306
Riboflavin (mg.)	1.31	0.72	0.8697	55	66

SOURCE: National Food Commission, *Estudo de Consumo de Alimentos . . .*
Boacica, Tables 44, 45, and 46.

*Error of new method is 0.45%.
†Amount of scarcest nutrient.

TABLE 4.3
Daily supplementary diet — poor families of Boacica
(per capita)

FOOD	QUANTITY	COST (CR $)
I — Economical supplementary diet (E.S. Diet) by new method* (selection procedure only)		
Sweet potato	100 grams	$ .50
Macassa beans	394 grams	$6.60
		total $7.10
II — Minimum cost supplementary diet (M.C.S. Diet) by linear programming		
Sweet potato	85 grams	$ .427
Macassa beans	393 grams	$6.576
		total $7.003

III — Nutritional data

DEFICIENT NUTRIENTS	ALLOWANCE	DEFICIENCY	PROVIDED BY E.S. DIET	PERCENT OF ALLOWANCE	
				Deficiency	Provided by E.S. Diet
Protein (gm.)	55.10	3.90	88.65	7	160
Calcium (mg.)	897.00	565.00	571.54†	63	63
Vitamin A (I. U.)	4251.00	510.00	578.14	12	13
Thiamin (mg.)	0.99	0.01	2.2152	1	223
Riboflavin (mg.)	1.35	0.62	0.7562	46	56

SOURCE: National Food Commission, *Estudo de Consumo de Alimentos . . . Boacica*, Tables 44, 45, and 46.

*Error of new method is 1.39%.
†Amount of the scarcest nutrient.

TABLE 4.4
Daily supplementary diet — very poor families of Santo Antônio (per capita)

FOOD	QUANTITY	COST (38 $)
I — Economical supplementary diet (E.S. Diet) by new method* (selection procedure only)		
Sweet potato	324 grams	$1.20
Fresh milk	397 grams	$3.90
		total $5.10
II — Minimum cost supplementary diet (M.C.S. Diet) by linear programming		
Sweet potato	299 grams	$1.109
Fresh milk	397 grams	$3.895
		total $5.004

III — Nutritional data

DEFICIENT NUTRIENTS	ALLOWANCE	DEFICIENCY	PROVIDED BY E.S. DIET	PERCENT OF ALLOWANCE	
				Deficiency	Provided by E.S. Diet
Calories (Cal.)	1895.00	360.00	467.600	19	24
Protein (gm.)	52.00	10.90	16.980	21	32
Calcium (mg.)	826.00	536.90	545.190†	65	66
Iron (mg.)	10.80	0.86	3.306	8	30
Vitamin A (I. U.)	3828.00	1071.80	1964.610	28	51
Thiamin (mg.)	0.91	0.39	0.4115	43	45
Riboflavin (mg.)	1.25	0.70	0.7941	56	63
Niacin (mg.)	9.30	1.30	2.3340	14	25

SOURCE: National Food Commission, *Inquérito de Alimentação . . . Santo Antônio*, Tables 30, 46, and 47.

*Error of new method is 1.92%.
†Amount of scarcest nutrient.

TABLE 4.5
Daily supplementary diet — poor families of Santo Antônio
(per capita)

FOOD	QUANTITY	COST (CR $)

I — Economical supplementary diet (E.S. Diet) by new method*
(selection procedure only)

FOOD	QUANTITY	COST
Sweet potato	172 grams	$0.60
Fresh milk	285 grams	$2.80
		total $3.40

II — Minimum cost supplementary diet (M.C.S. Diet) by linear programming

FOOD	QUANTITY	COST
Sweet potato	136 grams	$0.507
Fresh milk	286 grams	$2.802
		total $3.309

III — Nutritional data

DEFICIENT NUTRIENTS	ALLOWANCE	DEFICIENCY	PROVIDED BY E.S. DIET	PERCENT OF ALLOWANCE Deficiency	PERCENT OF ALLOWANCE Provided by E.S. Diet
Calories (Cal.)	1840.00	92.00	344.740	5	18
Protein (gm.)	52.20	7.30	11.346	14	21
Calcium (mg.)	842.00	362.00	369.580†	43	43
Vitamin A (I. U.)	4077.00	775.00	1086.260	19	26
Thiamin (mg.)	0.89	0.21	0.2326	24	26
Riboflavin (mg.)	1.27	0.48	0.5356	38	42

SOURCE: National Food Commission, *Inquérito de Alimentação Realizado em Santo Antônio,* Tables 30, 46, and 47.

*Error of new method is 2.75%.
†Amount of the scarcest nutrient.

58

TABLE 4.6
Daily supplementary diet — very poor families of São Paulo do Potengi (per capita)

FOOD	QUANTITY	COST (CR $)
I — Economical supplementary diet (E.S. Diet) by new method* (selection procedure only)		
Sweet potato	1889 grams	$10.20
II — Minimum cost supplementary diet (M.C.S. Diet) by linear programming		
Sweet potato	1875 grams	$10.122

III — Nutritional data

DEFICIENT NUTRIENTS	ALLOWANCE	DEFICIENCY	PROVIDED BY E.S. DIET	PERCENT OF ALLOWANCE Deficiency	Provided by E.S. Diet
Calories (Cal.)	1848.00	261.00	2040.000	14	110
Protein (gm.)	55.40	4.40	22.644	8	40
Calcium (mg.)	908.00	581.00	585.480†	64	64
Vitamin A (I. U.)	3912.00	391.00	8689.380	10	222
Thiamin (mg.)	1.15	0.21	1.7034	18	148
Riboflavin (mg.)	1.33	0.61	0.9486	46	71
Niacin (mg.)	10.70	1.80	11.322	17	105
Ascorbic acid (mg.)	56.00	9.00	398.780	16	712

SOURCE: National Food Commission, *Inquérito sôbre Hábitos . . . São Paulo do Potengi*, pp. 53, and 60-1.

*Error of new method is 0.77%.
†Amount of scarcest nutrient.

TABLE 4.7
Daily supplementary diet – poor families of São Paulo do Potengi (per capita)

I – Economical supplementary diet (E.S. Diet) by new method*
(selection procedure)

FOOD	QUANTITY	COST (CR $)
Sweet potato	1889 grams	$10.20
Pumpkin	49 grams	$ .50
	total	$10.70

Substituting Cr $ .10 sweet potato for Cr $ .50 pumpkin

Sweet potato	1908 grams	$10.30

II – Minimum cost supplementary diet (M.C.S. Diet) by linear programming

Sweet potato	1907 grams	$10.297

III – Nutritional data

DEFICIENT NUTRIENTS	ALLOWANCE	DEFICIENCY	PROVIDED BY E.S. DIET		PERCENT OF ALLOWANCE		
			Selection Procedure	Substitution Procedure	Deficiency	Provided by E.S. Diet Selection Procedure	Substitution Procedure
Calories (Cal.)	2145.00	21.0	2045.500	2060.000	1	95	96
Protein (gm.)	61.70	3.1	22.839	22.866	5	37	37
Calcium (mg.)	969.00	591.0	592.330	591.220†	61	61	61
Vitamin A (I.U.)	4419.00	1414.0	9729.980	8774.600	32	220	198
Riboflavin (mg.)	1.54	0.8	0.9876	0.9597	52	64	62
Niacin (mg.)	10.70	0.1	11.4370	11.4330	1	106	106

SOURCE: National Food Commission, *Inquérito sôbre Hábitos . . . São Paulo do Potengi*, pp. 53, and 60-1.

*Error of new method is 0.03%.
†Amounts of scarcest nutrient.

TABLE 4.8
Daily supplementary diet—very poor families of Currais (per capita)

FOOD	QUANTITY	COST (CR $)
I – Economical supplementary diet (E.S. Diet) by new method* (selection procedure)		
Macassa beans	54 grams	$1.30
Pumpkin	360 grams	$1.80
Fresh milk	359 grams	$6.60
		total $9.70
a) Substituting Cr $ .70 fresh milk for Cr $1.50 pumpkin		
Macassa beans	54 grams	$1.30
Pumpkin	60 grams	$ .30
Fresh milk	397 grams	$7.30
		total $8.90
b) Substituting Cr $ .80 fresh milk for Cr $ .80 macassa beans		
Macassa beans	21 grams	$ .50
Pumpkin	60 grams	$ .30
Fresh milk	431 grams	$8.10
		total $8.90
II – Minimum cost supplementary diet (M.C.S. Diet) by linear programming		
Macassa beans	20 grams	$ .479
Pumpkin	56 grams	$ .276
Fresh milk	429 grams	$8.045
		total $8.800

continued

TABLE 4.8—*continued*

III – Nutritional data

| DEFICIENT NUTRIENT | ALLOWANCE | DEFICIENCY | AMOUNT OF NUTRIENT PROVIDED BY E. S. DIET | | | PERCENT OF ALLOWANCE | | | |
| | | | Selection Procedure | Substitution Procedure a | Substitution Procedure b | Deficiency | Provided by E.S. Diet | | |
							Selection Procedure	Substitution Procedure a	Substitution Procedure b
Calories (Cal.)	1770.00	252.00	432.83	431.650	333.160	14	24	24	18
Protein (gm.)	55.30	14.40	25.35	25.418	19.442	26	45	45	35
Calcium (mg.)	890.00	525.00	526.57†	527.200	530.240†	59	59	59	59
Vitamin A (I.U.)	3682.00	663.00	8108.03	1769.740	1812.080	18	220	48	49
Thiamin (mg.)	0.94	0.11	0.5781	0.4393	0.1716	12	61	46	18
Riboflavin (mg.)	1.32	0.78	0.9597	0.7806†	0.7902	59	72	59	59
Niacin (mg.)	8.90	1.10	3.2140	1.8090	1.1450	12	36	20	12

SOURCE: National Food Commission, *Estudo da Alimentação . . . Currais*, Tables 50, 51, and 54.

*Error of new method is 1.14%.
†Amounts of scarcest nutrients.

TABLE 4.9
Cost of daily diet per capita
(Cr $)

VILLAGE	ACTUAL DIET*	M.C.S. DIET	SUPPLEMENTARY DIET AS PERCENT OF ACTUAL DIET
Poor			
Santo Antônio	$14.33	$ 3.309	23
Boacica	23.98	7.003	29
São Paulo do Potengi	31.08	10.297	33
Very poor			
Santo Antônio	15.19	5.004	32
Boacica	18.00	8.163	45
São Paulo do Potengi	24.46	10.122	41
Currais	18.30	8.800	48

*Santo Antônio: National Food Commission, *Inquérito de Alimentação Realizado em Santo Antônio*, Table 33.

Boacica: National Food Commission, *Estudo de Consumo de Alimentos . . . Boacica*, Table 38.

São Paulo do Potengi: National Food Commission, *Inquérito sôbre Hábitos . . . São Paulo do Potengi*, Table 37.

Currais: National Food Commission, *Estudo da Alimentação . . . Currais*, Table 45.

very poor families increases from 649.69 to 651.68 milligrams, and the amount of vitamin A decreases from 1139.9 to 949.69 I.U., which is smaller than the 1077 I.U. deficiency. For the poor families the amount of calcium increases from 571.14 to 573.73 milligrams, and the amount of vitamin A decreases from 578.14 to 478.33 I.U., which is smaller than the 565 I.U. deficiency. To reproduce these calculations use the data in lines 2 and 3, columns 1 and 2 of Table 4.1. In the supplementary diets for Santo Antônio (Tables 4.4 and 4.5), when trying to substitute Cr $.10 of fresh milk for Cr $.10 of sweet potato, the level of calcium increases, but the amount of thiamin becomes smaller than its allowance. There is only one food in the supplementary diet of the very poor families of São Paulo do Potengi (Table 4.6). In none of the above five supplementary diets, therefore, is substitution among foods possible.

Substitutions are possible in economical supplementary diets for the poor families of São Paulo do Potengi and for the very poor families of Currais (Tables 4.7 and 4.8). They also present the minimum cost supplementary diets computed by linear programming, using the amounts of the deficiencies as the quantities of nutrients to be provided.

For the poor families of São Paulo do Potengi (Table 4.7) the scarcest nutrient is calcium. At the prices prevalent in this village it is possible to obtain either 5.74 milligrams or 1.37 milligrams of calcium by spending Cr $.10 on sweet potato or pumpkin, respectively. Then, by substituting Cr $.10 worth of sweet potato for Cr $.10 worth of pumpkin, the level of calcium in the supplementary diet increases. As the amounts of the other nutrients do not become smaller than their allowances, such substitution is permissible and if made, could reduce the cost of this diet.

For the very poor families of Currais (Table 4.8) the scarcest nutrient is also calcium. It is possible to obtain either 5.71 milligrams, 2.8 milligrams or 6.09 milligrams of calcium by spending Cr $.10 on macassa beans, pumpkin or fresh milk, respectively. Then substituting Cr $.10 worth of fresh milk for Cr $.10 worth of macassa beans or pumpkin, or Cr $.10 worth of macassa beans for Cr $.10 worth of pumpkin, increases the level of calcium in the supplementary diet. As the amounts of the other nutrients do not become smaller than their allowances, such substitutions are permissible and if made, could reduce the cost of this diet.

Keeping the level of the scarcest nutrient unchanged allows one to withdraw an amount of food that is greater in monetary cost than the amount being added. Thus the cost of the diet is reduced. The substitution goes on until the food being withdrawn is completely excluded from the diet or the amount of some other nutrient becomes smaller than its allowance. This leads to Rule 5:

RULE 5. *The rate of substitution between two foods in the supplementary diet is:*

$$\frac{\text{amount of food}}{\text{amount of food}} = \frac{\text{amount of scarcest nutrient in one value unit of food being added}}{\text{amount of scarcest nutrient in one value unit of food being withdrawn}}$$

The substitution takes place until the food being withdrawn is totally excluded from the supplementary diet or the amount of some other nutrient is reduced to the level of its allowance. Then go back to Rule 4.

For the poor families of São Paulo do Potengi, the substitution rate of sweet potato for pumpkin is 4.19, given by the ratio of the amounts of calcium supplied by Cr $.10 worth of sweet potato and pumpkin (5.74/1.37). For simplicity in calculation, use the largest multiple of Cr $.10 that is smaller than the rate of substitution. Thus, it is possible to increase the expenditure on sweet potato by Cr $.10 and decrease the expenditure on pumpkin by Cr $.40, without reducing the level of calcium in the supplementary diet. As there is an excess of calcium from the selection phase to start with, and the rate of substitution is not fully used, one can then take out another Cr $.10 worth of pumpkin from the supplementary diet, without reducing the level of any nutrient to an amount smaller than the allowance. This excludes pumpkin from the diet. The cost of the supplementary diet is reduced from Cr $10.70 to Cr $10.30. Rule 4 cannot be applied again, because there is now only one food in this diet.

For the very poor families of Currais, the rates of substitution of fresh milk for pumpkin or macassa beans, and of macassa beans for pumpkin, are 2.17, 1.06 and 2.03, given by the ratios of the amounts of calcium supplied by Cr $.10 worth of fresh milk and pumpkin (6.09/ 2.8), fresh milk and macassa beans (6.09/5.71), and macassa beans and pumpkin (5.71/2.8), respectively. Start the substitution process with fresh milk and pumpkin, because this gives the largest rate of substitution and thus the largest saving for each substitution. For simplicity in calculation use the largest multiple of Cr $.10 that is smaller than the rate of substitution. Thus it is possible to increase the expenditure on fresh milk by Cr $.10 and decrease the expenditure on pumpkin by Cr $.20, without reducing the level of calcium in the supplementary diet.

At the eighth substitution the level of riboflavin becomes smaller than its allowance, so only seven substitutions are possible. As there is an excess of calcium from the selection procedure to start with and the rate of substitution is not fully used, one can take out still another Cr $.10 worth of pumpkin from the supplementary diet without reducing the level of any nutrient to an amount smaller than the allowance. Then the cost of this diet is reduced from Cr $9.70 to Cr $8.90.

The scarcest nutrient now becomes riboflavin. It is possible to obtain .0075 milligrams, .016 milligrams, or .0087 milligrams of riboflavin by spending Cr $.10 on macassa beans, pumpkin, or fresh milk, respectively. By substituting Cr $.10 worth of pumpkin for Cr $.10 worth of macassa beans or fresh milk, the level of riboflavin increases, but the amount of calcium in the diet becomes smaller than its allowance. These substitutions are not possible. By substituting Cr $.10 worth of fresh milk for Cr $.10 worth of macassa beans, the riboflavin level increases without making the level of any other nutrient smaller than the allowance. This substitution is permissible. If made, it would reduce the cost of this diet.

The rate of substitution of fresh milk for macassa beans is 1.16, given by the ratio of the amount of riboflavin furnished by Cr $.10 worth of fresh milk and macassa beans (.0087/.0075). For simplicity in calculation, use the largest multiple of Cr $.10 that is smaller than the substitution ratio. It is possible to increase the expenditure on fresh milk by Cr $.10 and decrease the expenditure on macassa beans by Cr $.10 without reducing the riboflavin level. It is obvious that substituting Cr $.10 of fresh milk for Cr $.10 of macassa beans does not reduce the cost of the supplementary diet. However, such substitutions may build up excesses that allow one to withdraw one value unit of food being withdrawn without adding on value unit of the food being added. This would reduce the cost of the diet by one value unit.

At the ninth substitution the amount of niacin becomes smaller than its allowance, thus only eight substitutions are possible. This result can be checked, knowing that by spending Cr $.10 of macassa beans, pumpkin or fresh milk, it is possible to obtain .088 milligram, .1 milligram, or .005 milligram of niacin, respectively. As it is no longer possible to reduce the cost of the diet by at least one full step (Cr $.10), return to Rule 4. Other substitutions are still possible, but none of them allows the cost of the diet to be reduced by a full step. Therefore, this economical supplementary diet is left as it is after the last substitution.

Note that there can be more than one "scarcest nutrient." This makes this method much more difficult to operate, because it is necessary to pay attention to all the scarcest nutrients at the same time.

Instead of using steps of Cr $.10, if one had used smaller steps such as Cr $.01 for example, the excess nutrients provided in the selection phase would be smaller. The smaller steps would also allow more precise results in the substitution procedure.

THE EXPENDITURE ON FOOD

When food habits are not taken into account, still more economical diets can be obtained by drastically changing the proportions in which the existing foods are being consumed. Some foods may even be excluded from the diet entirely. By employing linear programming, it would be possible to obtain the least-cost diet providing the recommended allowances of all the essential nutrients, but it is questionable that families would accept such least-cost diets. Supplementary diets should be acceptable, however, because they do not require giving up any existing consumption. The foods in the economical supplementary diets suggested in this study are chosen from some twenty eligible foods widely consumed in the villages, so, these supplementary diets take the food habits of the families into account.

It is important to know how much the cost of each supplementary diet is in comparison with the cost of each existing diet. Table 4.9

shows the daily cost of the existing diet on a per capita basis and compares it with the per capita minimum cost supplementary diet (obtained by linear programming) for each of the families studied. The supplementary diet that represents the smallest increase in the existing expenditure on foods is for the poor families of Santo Antônia, where it is 23 percent of the actual cost. Considering that the families studied were poor or very poor and in an underdeveloped area, it is hardly conceivable that they could afford such additions to their food budgets.

If the families decide to spend an additional amount of money that is smaller than the minimum cost supplementary diet, but hope to improve their nutritional status as much as possible, this can be done with a small modification of the method developed in the study.

Considering that all the nutrients have equal intrinsic importance, assume the nutritional function (I):

$$S = (100n_1 - \tfrac{1}{2}n_1^2) + \ldots + (100n_h - \tfrac{1}{2}n_h^2) + (m - h)5000$$

when $n_i > 100$, take $n_i = 100$.

The new modified method used Rules 1 and 2 of the selection procedure. Rule 3 can still be used until all the available money is depleted, however, in this case, it is not possible to eliminate all the deficiencies.

After the selection procedure, see whether substituting one value unit of a food for one value unit of another food will increase the value of the function (I). This substitution keeps the amount of money unchanged, leading to the following rules:

RULE 4A. *Calculate the nutritional contributions of foods at the end of the selection procedure. See whether at this point, the contributions of all the foods in the supplementary diet are equal (or approximately equal). See whether the nutritional contributions of the foods not selected are smaller than the ones in the diet. If this occurs, the nutritional function (I) is at the attainable maximum or close to it.*

RULE 5A. *When the condition in Rule 4A is not satisfied, substitute one value unit (Cr $.10, for example) of the food with*

> *the largest nutritional contribution for one value unit of the food in the diet with the smallest nutritional contribution. Continue this substitution process until the condition in Rule 4A is met.*

Rule 4A is a paraphrase of a very familiar conclusion of economic analysis. The consumer maximizes his nutritional function (I) (utility function), subject to a budget constraint, when the nutritional contributions per unit of money (marginal utilities per dollar) of the foods in the diets are equal. The nutritional contributions per unit of money (marginal utilities per dollar) of the foods not contained in the diet are smaller than those for the foods in the supplementary diet.

In short, this alternate method considers the intake of all nutrients equal to zero so that at the starting of the calculations, each nutrient has a deficiency equal to 100. When the consumer has an amount of money to spend on food that is smaller than the one required by the minimum cost diet given by linear programming, the new modified method employing Rules 4A and 5A gives a diet that approximately maximizes his nutritional status as represented by function (I).

5

CONCLUSION

. . . .

CONSIDERING THAT NUTRITIONISTS ARE NOT ABLE TO SAY THAT ONE nutrient is intrinsically more important than another one, the deficiency-weighted sum of nutrients is an appropriate measurement of the nutritional contributions of foods. This measure can only be used when the intake is smaller than the recommended allowance of at least one nutrient.

In countries or regions of a country in which deficiencies exist, the resources available are generally very scarce and must be efficiently allocated so that the state of poverty can be eradicated as quickly as possible.

THEORETICAL APPLICATIONS

Suppose a certain amount of resources is designated for food production research and development for example. Having a measure of the nutritional contributions of foods, the research and development can be concentrated on a few foods that have the largest nutritional contributions.

Suppose that the government decides to start a campaign to introduce new foods into the actual consumption pattern of the population. This measure will select the foods with the largest nutritional contributions, taking the food habits of the population into account. For instance, beef is not acceptable for most Indians and a campaign for its introduction into the food consumption pattern of the Indian population is bound to fail. The introduction of these foods will yield the largest improvement in the nutritional status of the population for each dollar spent on such a campaign.

When additional resources become available for expanding the production of foods, having the production functions (or approximations) for the foods, the measure will indicate the foods giving the largest nutritional contributions per unit of additional resources employed.

If the countries or regions of a country in which deficiencies prevail want to import foods to improve the nutritional status of their populations, then the measure can be used to indicate the foods with the largest nutritional contributions per unit of foreign exchange.

For countries like the U.S. that provide food aid to underdeveloped nations, the measure points out which foods have the largest nutritional contributions for a specific underdeveloped country. The measure can also be employed to select the country where a particular food can be of most nutritional benefit.

FURTHER ASPECTS

Many other applications and policies can be formulated for a measure of the nutritional contributions of foods. The method developed in this study to obtain economical diets for use in improving the nutritional status of the populations of poorer regions may be very useful because it does not need skilled personnel for its computation. With the measure proposed, such regions may become more efficient when employing their scarce resources on activities related to feeding human beings.

BIBLIOGRAPHY

Armstrong, J. G. "An Economic-Nutritional Index of Foods." *Canadian Nutrition Notes* 22(1966): 25-39.

Black, J. D. *Food Enough*. Science for War and Peace Series. Lancaster, Penn.: The Jacques Cattell Press, 1943.

Black, J. D., and Kiefer, M. E. *Future Food and Agriculture Policy*. New York, London and Toronto: McGraw-Hill Book Co., Inc., 1948.

Christensen, R. P. *Using Resources to Meet Food Needs*. Washington, D.C.: U.S. Department of Agriculture Bureau of Agricultural Economics, U.S. Government Printing Office, 1943.

————. *Efficient Use of Land Resources in the United States*. Washington, D.C.: U.S. Department of Agriculture Technical Bulletin 963, U.S. Government Printing Office, 1948.

Cooper, M. C., and Spillman, W. J. *Human Food from an Acre of Staple Farm Products*. Washington, D.C.: U.S. Department of Agriculture Farmers' Bulletin 877, U.S. Government Printing Office, 1917.

Davis, J. G. "The Nutritional Index and the Economic Nutritional Index of Foods." *Dairy Industries* 30(1965) 193-7.

Kaplan, W. *Advanced Calculus*. Reading, Mass.: Addison-Wesley Publishing Co., Inc., 1959.

Lancaster, K. J. "A New Approach to Consumer Theory." *Journal of Political Economy* 74(1966): 132-57.

Mighell, R. L., and Christensen, R. P. "Measuring Maximum Contributions to Food Needs by Producing Areas." *Journal of Farm Economics* 26(1944): 181-95.

National Food Commission. *Estudo da Alimentaçao e das Condiçoes Econômico-Sociais Realisado no Povoado de Currais, Municipio de Nisia Floresta-Rio Grande do Norte (Brasil), Agôsto de 1961.* Brazil: Ministry of Health, National Food Commission, 1961.

————. *Estudo de Consumo de Alimentos e das Condiçoes Socio-Econômicas nas Familias Representativas de Povoado de Boacica, Município de Touros, Rio Grande do Norte, Brasil, Novembro de 1960.* Brazil: Ministry of Health National Food Commission, 1960.

————. *Inquérito de Alimentaçao Realizado em Santo Antônio, Estado de Rio Grande do Norte (Brasil), Novembro de 1959.* Brazil: Ministry of Health, National Food Commission, 1959.

————. *Inquérite sôbre Hábitos e Recursos Alimentares, Sao Paulo do Potengi, Rio Grande do Norte, Brazil.* Brazil: Ministry of Health, National Food Commission, 1961.

National Research Council, Food and Nutrition Board. *Recommended Dietary Allowances.* Washington, D.C.: National Research Council Publication No. 589, National Academy of Sciences, 1958.

Sherman, H. D., and Gillet, L. R. *The Adequacy and Economy of Some City Dietaries.* New York: New York Association for Improving the Condition of the Poor, Publication 121, 1917.

Smith, V.E. "Measurement of Product Attributes Recognized by Consumers." In *Seminar on Consumer Preferences and Market Development for Farm Products,* CAEA Report 5. Ames, Iowa: Iowa State University of Science and Technology Center for Agricultural and Economic Adjustment, 1960.

————. *Electronic Computation of Human Diets.* East Lansing: Division of Research, Graduate School of Business Administration, Michigan State University, 1964.

Stamp, L. D. "The Measurement of Land Resources." *Geographical Review* 48(1958): 1-15.

Stigler, G. J. "The Cost of Subsistence." *Journal of Farm Economics* 27(1945): 303-14.

Terroine, E. F. "Valeur Aliméntaire et Coût des Denrées." *Annales de la Nutrition et de l'Aliméntation* 16(1962): 91-172.

Tremolières, J., Serville, Y., and Jacquot, R. *La Pratique de l'Aliméntation.* 2nd ed. vol. 3. Paris: Les Éditions Sociales Françaises, 1962.

U.S. Interdepartmental Committee for Nutrition and National Development. *Northeast Brazil, Nutrition Survey, March-May 1963.* Washington, D.C.: May 1965.

Wilson, E. D., Fisher, K. H., and Fuqua, M. E. *Principles of Nutrition.* New York: John Wiley & Sons, Inc., 1959.

Zobler, L. "A New Measure of Food Production Efficiency." *Geographical Review* 31(1961): 549-69.

PUBLICATIONS

of the division of research

. . . .

Bureau of Business and Economic Research

MSU BUSINESS STUDIES

ELEMENTARY MATHEMATICS OF LINEAR
PROGRAMMING AND GAME THEORY
Edward G. Bennion

EXPLORATIONS IN RETAILING
Stanley C. Hollander

MARGINAL ASPECTS OF MANAGEMENT PRACTICES
Frederic N. Firestone

CONTRIBUTIONS OF FOUR ACCOUNTING PIONEERS
James Don Edwards, Roland F. Salmonson

LIFE INSURANCE COMPANIES IN THE CAPITAL MARKET
Andrew F. Brimmer

THE AUTOMOTIVE CAREER OF RANSOM E. OLDS
Glenn A. Niemeyer

ELECTRONIC COMPUTATION OF HUMAN DIETS
Victor E. Smith

INTERNATIONAL ENTERPRISE IN A DEVELOPING ECONOMY
*Claude McMillan, Jr., Richard F. Gonzalez
with Leo G. Erickson*

THE ENTERPRISING MAN
Orvis F. Collins, David G. Moore with Darab B. Unwalla

AGRICULTURAL MARKET ANALYSIS
Vernon L. Sorenson, editor

LABOR MARKET INSTITUTIONS AND WAGES IN THE
LODGING INDUSTRY
John P. Henderson

75

THE EXECUTIVE IN CRISIS
Eugene Emerson Jennings

BANKING STRUCTURE IN MICHIGAN: 1945-1963
Robert F. Lanzillotti

RETAIL DECENTRALIZATION
Eli P. Cox, Leo G. Erickson

BANK ADMINISTERED POOLED EQUITY FUNDS FOR
EMPLOYEE BENEFIT PLANS
Frank L. Voorheis

THE PERFORMANCE POST AUDIT IN STATE GOVERNMENT
Lennis M. Knighton

PASSENGER TRANSPORTATION
Stanley C. Hollander

THE EFFECTS OF DATA-PROCESSING SERVICE BUREAUS ON
THE PRACTICE OF PUBLIC ACCOUNTING
Constantine Konstans

A SELECTED AND ANNOTATED BIBLIOGRAPHY
ON SHOPPING CENTER MANAGEMENT
Bernard J. LaLonde, Paul E. Smith

WORK ROLE INVOLVEMENT OF INDUSTRIAL SUPERVISORS
John G. Maurer

SELECTION OF NEW SUPPLIES BY THE MOBILE FAMILY
James E. Bell, Jr.

THE CHECKLESS SOCIETY: ITS COST IMPLICATIONS FOR THE FIRM
William H. Mateer

MEASURING PERFORMANCE IN MULTI-OUTLET BUSINESSES
William R. Kinney, Jr.

DEPARTMENT STORE MERCHANDISING IN CHANGING ENVIRONMENTS
Louis H. Grossman

THE FORMULATION OF EXPECTED INTEREST RATES:
AN EXAMINATION OF ALTERNATIVE HYPOTHESES
Frank J. Bonello

Institute for International Business and Economic Development Studies

MSU INTERNATIONAL BUSINESS AND ECONOMIC STUDIES

MICHIGAN'S COMMERCE AND COMMERCIAL POLICY STUDY
John L. Hazard

INTERNATIONAL DIMENSIONS IN BUSINESS
Recent Readings from Business Topics

MANAGEMENT DEVELOPMENT AND EDUCATION IN THE
SOVIET UNION
Barry M. Richman

THE UNITED STATES OVERSEAS EXECUTIVE:
HIS ORIENTATIONS AND CAREER PATTERNS
Richard F. Gonzalez, Anant R. Negandhi

STEEL AND ECONOMIC DEVELOPMENT: CAPITAL-OUTPUT
RATIOS IN THREE LATIN AMERICAN STEEL PLANTS
David G. Greene

ALTERNATIVE COMMERCIAL POLICIES — THEIR EFFECT
ON THE AMERICAN ECONOMY
Mordechai E. Kreinin

INSTITUTION BUILDING IN BUSINESS ADMINISTRATION —
THE BRAZILIAN EXPERIENCE
Donald A. Taylor

THE OPTIMAL STAGING AND PHASING OF MULTI-PRODUCT CAPACITY
Harold H. Wein, V. P. Sreedharan

EDUCATION FOR BUSINESS IN A DEVELOPING SOCIETY
Amar N. Agarwalla

Institute of Public Utilities

MSU PUBLIC UTILITIES STUDIES

DEVELOPMENT OF SEPARATIONS PRINCIPLES IN THE
TELEPHONE INDUSTRY
Richard Gabel

PERFORMANCE UNDER REGULATION
Harry M. Trebing, editor

MID-CONTINENT AREA POWER PLANNERS
W. Stewart Nelson

RATE OF RETURN UNDER REGULATION:
NEW DIRECTIONS AND PERSPECTIVES
Harry M. Trebing, R. Hayden Howard, editors

MSU PUBLIC UTILITIES PAPERS

SELECTED STRUCTURE AND ALLOCATION
PROBLEMS IN THE REGULATED INDUSTRIES
Manley R. Irwin, Milton Russell

DATE DUE